The
Baby
Box

The
Baby
Box

A TRUE STORY

Jane Hayward

Matador
9 Priory Business Park,
Wistow Road, Kibworth Beauchamp,
Leicestershire., LE8 0RX
Tel: 0116 279 2299
Email: books@troubador.co.uk
Web: www.troubador.co.uk/matador
Twitter: @matadorbooks

ISBN 978 1789016 871

British Library Cataloguing in Publication Data.
A catalogue record for this book is available from the British Library.

Printed and bound in Great Britain by 4edge Limited
Typeset in 11pt Adobe Garamond Pro by Troubador Publishing Ltd, Leicester, UK

Matador is an imprint of Troubador Publishing Ltd

This book is dedicated to all the young women dubbed unmarried mothers during the heady days of the 1960s.

And to all those given away in adoption, who are still wondering if their birth mothers loved them.

FOREWORD

This is the true story of the stormy relationship between my mother and me, during the so-called permissive society of the mid-sixties. It centres on two years of my teenage life, some episodes fun and free, some shocking and distressful, but many full of a certain kind of joy.

I have been blessed with a good memory. I can conjure up scenes full of drama, the sounds, sights and smells, even the very words spoken. I have turned my memoir into a dramatic narrative, because I want you to enjoy this book.

One

Monday 21 December 1964
The House of Commons votes for the abolition of the death penalty. I've got more to worry about than the fate of criminals. I've got my own life to save.

My mother says, 'If you'd cut me up in little pieces, you couldn't have hurt me more.'

It's Christmas Eve and we're in our lounge, alone. I'm used to my mother's sharp tongue. She's been using it against me since I reached puberty. 'Stand up straight.' 'Who said you could use lipstick? With that stuff smeared all over your mouth, you look like a trollop.'

My latest crime is much worse than stooping as I walk or experimenting with makeup. This is a life-changing crisis. There can be no going back.

Mum is staring at me, blinking, but not to keep her tears back. She blinks when she's so angry she can hardly control herself. Her anger is all my fault. I watch her, not knowing what to say.

I wish I could turn the clock back to just over a week ago.

The heavy door of the school library swings shut behind me as I tiptoe into the silence of twenty-five girls, with heads bent, intent on reading and writing. I creep to an empty table and sit down. Opening my rough notebook next to my Bible makes me feel virtuous. I enjoy scripture, although I've given up chatting to God as He's clearly given up looking out for me. I stare at the question set for holiday prep.

Consider the lilies of the field. Why did Jesus choose them to illustrate his message?

For a few minutes I forget while I draw lilies: heavy, white blooms, stylized flowers in the middle of the paper. Clear. Clean. Innocent. A gremlin in my head adds their yellow stigma, waiting to be fertilized by the male pollen. What difference will five pages covered with words make now? I scribble a one-line answer: Because lilies are the symbol of virginity and what is more important than virginity?

Surely love is more important than virginity? I flick the pages of my Bible, searching for some authority to tell me I haven't got it wrong. Love is what matters.

My petty attempt at philosophy is interrupted by someone stomping her thick-heeled shoes on the wooden floor until they reach my table. I shut my holy book and look up.

Rita. Rita is a mod: her black hair cut in a blunt bob, her face pale with pan stick and her short legs fettered by her calf length navy skirt. She isn't my best friend because I don't have one, but we catch the same bus as she lives just around the corner from me.

Rita's house has a front garden cluttered with thistles, those daisy-like weeds and beer cans. Steps lead up to the front door. One morning I called for her. The front door was opened by a weedy looking woman with a lighted cigarette between her lips. 'She ain't ready. Come up.' She turned. The back of her once-white toweling dressing gown was marked with dried blood stains. I blushed.

The hall was gloomy and depressing with its musty, almost sickening sweet smell. I'd never been in a house like that or guessed that a girl who'd passed the eleven plus would live like this. I followed Rita's mother up the stairs. The thin carpet was so faded I could only guess at its original colour and even then it seemed to be a muddy beige. As we reached the turn of the half-landing, the smell became distinct. Stale urine. We passed an open door. The lavatory. With no seat on the pedestal and a flooded floor, the roll of paper lying there, sodden.

On the next landing, the woman pushed open a door with a Yale lock. I followed her into the large front room with a sash window. In one corner stood a cooker and a sink. In another, a sofa sat opposite a television. In the centre, a shabby table and three chairs. As I took in the sordid details, any delusions I'd harboured about living in a flat, absorbed from American sit-coms on the telly with wall-to-wall carpets and glitzy kitchens, were banished.

'Hi,' said Rita's voice. 'Just getting my stuff.'

In the far, gloomy corner was a single bed, the candlewick bedspread covered with school books. Rita's bed. Rita slept in here, with the gas cooker and the TV. Noisy and maybe dangerous. I was sure I could smell gas.

A half-open door on the far side of the room was suddenly pulled back. A man clothed in a grey vest and a pair of pyjama trousers stood in the opening. Even in the dim light I could see he hadn't shaved for several days.

'For heaven's sake, Dad,' Rita said too quickly. 'Have some shame.'

He took a step back and slammed the door.

As we were going downstairs, the ghastly truth dawned on me: Rita shared that leaking lavatory with strangers. I wished I could wave a magic wand and make everything come right.

Rita had her own way of making things come right. She might be a mod but she didn't go in for fighting. Loving was more her style, if you could call it that. One day, she'd turned up at school sporting a leather jacket, cut in a boxy style. The following week it was a chunky ruby ring set in gold. Expensive. I hung around the cloakroom with the others, impressed. Rita leapt onto a wooden bench to strut up and down pushing the shoe bags out of her way. Beaming, she looked extraordinarily proud of herself. 'The very latest, no rubbish.'

Yesterday morning we'd grabbed the top front seat. Rita followed her routine, flipping open her shoulder bag (regulation navy, but a spacious, proper, grown-up bag) pushing her books aside, searching for a small mirror, a comb and her makeup. After a quick back-comb of her hair, she spat on a black block of mascara, rubbed the stiff brush against it and then swept the stuff onto her lashes.

As she worked, she boasted. 'I told him, it's a pair of boots or you're not getting it.'

I was mesmerized. 'Will he buy them for you?'

'Got to hasn't he? All blokes want the same thing but you're a good girl so you won't know that.'

I'd kept dumb.

◆ ◆ ◆

Now, Rita dumps her bag on my table and leans over to read my notebook. 'No one round here knows what a virgin is.' She lowers her voice. 'Except you.'

Rita doesn't know everything.

I consider the alternative essay subject. Describe the feeding of the five thousand and discuss how the miracle... *Forget discussing miracles. Dear God, just send me one.*

Rita perches on the chair next to me and opens her rough notebook. She scribbles, What are you doing for Xmas?

I stare at the simple question. I have the simple answer. Rita will know eventually. Everyone will know eventually. I scribble back, Leaving school.

Rita's face is a fair impersonation of Bambi, all wide eyes and open mouth. 'Why?'

I'll never see Rita after the end of this term. She's a safe person to confide in, she won't think the worst of me. I need to say the words out loud before I repeat them to my mother.

'I'm pregnant.'

Rita colours, enough for me to understand her shock. She gazes at my face as if summing up this new me. 'There was me thinking you were a good girl.'

She opens her bag and turfs out a German dictionary, a plastic make-up bag, a Mars bar and finally a small round cardboard box. Its top is scuffed, its edges worn down.

Without a word, she takes off the lid, tips out large white pills, convex like double sided flying saucers, and pushes one towards me. The tablet, lying not an inch from my notebook, is larger than an aspirin, with a shiny and grubby coating. It looks stale. Unappetising.

'I've used them twice,' Rita says. 'They work.'

Trust Rita, the little navy-blue clad mod, to have stuff like this. Forget fags. Push purple hearts to the back burner. Anyone can have those. Only Rita would have an illegal, do-it-yourself, do-away-with-it kit in her school bag. She pushes it closer. 'Before it's too late.'

I don't ask her why she thinks it's not too late, or even when too late is. I can't pick it up. I'm afraid.

Thrusting her hand into her school bag again, Rita produces a penknife. Cut in half, the tablet spills its innards on the table. Brown powder. Like cocoa. 'It'll get rid of it.'

Rita means kill it.

I know about small dead things. When I was eight, Mum gave me a kitten for my birthday, said I was old enough for the responsibility. My kitten ran between my legs to be hit by a car. The body hung over my hand, limp, like an old teddy which had lost its stuffing. Its mouth was open. I saw blood on its tongue. I hugged my pet to me, keeping it warm, trying to revive it. The kitten stayed dead.

What if the tablet doesn't work? I'll spend the next six months waiting for a monster. We had a girl at my primary school who had deformed hands and feet. No one spoke to her. No one. All day. What if my baby turns out like that girl? My baby. As I think the words my baby, the growth in my womb changes from a what into a who.

I refuse to poison my baby. I don't bother arguing with Rita. I push the ruined tablet away.

Rita scoops the powder into her hand. 'They're expensive, you know.' Although she tips the mess into the waste-paper basket, she doesn't sound cross.

At a quarter to four, I come out of school, dawdling along the pavement, gazing at scenes of caring mothers meeting first years, asking if they'd had a good day, had they eaten their lunch. Groups of chattering seniors, swapping ideas about homework essays, giggling over new boyfriends. The world of happy families, the fantasy world of laughter and fun, not the real world of fears and doubts.

I vow I'll tell Mum the minute I get home. No need to be apprehensive. Mum loves me. She loves babies. Everything will be arranged, the wedding, where we'll live, the whole lot. Mum will see to that. She's good at settling things, my mother.

Rita catches me up. She gives me a quick look. 'Can I tell the others? Just for a laugh?'

What others? All the girls in our form or just her special drug-taking mates? For a laugh? That hurts. She doesn't understand after all. She's only concerned with being the first to shout out my news. To humiliate me. Because I will be humiliated. Everyone will know I'm still an innocent. I've got the whole growing up thing wrong. Especially the love thing. Love is pink and glorious. Love is about wandering into the sunset with the boy who wants to hold your hand; three steps to heaven with the boy who thinks you are his girl. It isn't supposed to bring nights of worry, wondering what to do, what will happen next. Rita's cruel laughter proves I'm still a little girl. A little girl who needs her mother.

Any idea of chatting to Him-up-There is a complete non-starter. I know the rules. Transgress and thou will be punished. Not that I see my baby as punishment. My punishment is the shame I'll bring on my mum's head.

Rita's parting shot of advice is, 'You'll be OK. Your mum's decent.'

Was what I had done decent? Not in my mother's eyes. Is being a pregnant schoolgirl decent? Not even in my eyes.

As I shut the door of the house, my good resolution is smothered by domesticity. The chip pan is sizzling on the cooker; I can smell the fish under the grill. I nip up to my room, flick the switch on my record player and put on an Elvis 45. A Mess of Blues fits my mood.

In my diary I write, 'Rita made me ashamed. I am sorry. Mum will understand. She loves me, doesn't she?'

Next morning, the smell of frying bacon, a Saturday treat for my father, makes me retch. My mother eating a soft-boiled egg, the click of her dentures, threatens me with throw-up. Only my stomach is empty, so I can't. I ladle sugar into my tea with careless abandon.

I run the words through in my head. *Mum, I need your help. I'm in a mess.* But I don't share Rita's faith she'll be

OK. I can't believe my upright mother will hug me and say, We'll manage. My mother's good at managing but only if the reward's high enough. She isn't good at dealing with the unexpected, particularly when it makes her look less than she'd like to be. Her pride in moving to her posh house will not withstand her humiliation, when she learns I am that lowest of the low, a pregnant schoolgirl.

The first photo album I had, when I was about twelve years old, was a scrap book, its cover illustrated with bright red and yellow images of a group of teenagers enjoying a boat ride. I fitted my photos, taken with my father's Box Brownie, into white corner pieces stuck carefully on the soft grey paper. I still have that book, although now the pages are made secure by sticky tape and several of the frames are empty.

I'm about four years old, dressed in a knitted bathing suit patterned with rabbits. Even in a black and white print, it is clear I have fair hair. The picture is small but the memory vivid. My mother holds the camera. 'Smile Jane.' Days of sunshine and innocence.

Turning the pages brings a much later summer. The photos document my adolescence. I am on a beach wearing my first bikini, so about fourteen. Then at the tennis club dance in a red shot taffeta dress my mother made for me. She had tried, my mother, until it really mattered, until trying was impossible for her, too much for her sense of propriety, for her belief in what was respectable.

The photographs continue to tell their story: the summer of 1963, a school trip to a Roman villa. I'm in a line of girls wearing cotton skirts pushed out by layers of white net petticoats. Finally, a shot of me flinging my school beret into the river. We were about to move to London, which was the start of it all.

Saturday, 24 August 1963.
We've moved to Streatham but it's not proper London at all. We should be living in one of those houses in films, tall and elegant with long windows and iron railings, left over from centuries ago, but instead I'm in a suburban semi with white painted window frames and a fake lantern outside the front door. The front garden is just a path and shrubs. The road's called Warwick Avenue but there isn't a tree in sight.

My mother loved that house, set in an area called Clapham Park. She meandered from room to room, planning to make loose covers for the sitting room chairs. I was instructed not to clutter the hall, complete with a console table for the telephone.

Not that she was entirely satisfied. 'The people who sold us this house have moved to the other side of the common,' she told me. 'It's a smarter area than here, nearer to Pratt's.'

Pratt's was the posh department store. Poor Mum. Even with my father's promotion and her new home, her dream was not yet fulfilled.

My mother's dream was that I grew up to be a model of correctness according to her rules, garnered from small-time village life and punitive church doctrine. I was to fulfil her ideals of an obedient daughter without rebellion, skipping my teenage years and jumping straight from an innocent child to a modest virgin bride.

Wednesday 11 September 1963
Start new school tomorrow. No uniform in the sixth!
Mum bought me a fab white blouse with a pointed
collar, a navy pleated skirt, and made a duffle bag
for my books. Wonder what the other girls will be
like. Mum said to take some knitting and then I'll get
asked what I'm making. Good idea.

It's a Friday afternoon and I'm late home. Since hanging around street corners is a venal offence by my mother's rules, I'm frantically trying to think of an excuse. I mutter *Dear God, make the bus come.* No answer. The minutes gather together. The begging changes to accusation. *Where are you, on a tea break?*

As I push open the front door, I'm greeted by a drifting smog, stained brown. My mother hasn't smoked for years and, for just a second, I wonder what's going on.

Then a familiar voice. 'Is that Jane?'

I remember. Fiona, Mum's friend from her war days, my godmother, has come to see the new house. I'm saved. I hang my duffle coat on the bannister and dump my bag on the bottom stair.

In the lounge, Fiona, wearing a fitted suit, pale blue wool, its edges outlined with black braid, is straight from *Vogue*. Her blonde bob has flicked ends, her eyes are outlined in black and her lipstick is a fashionable pink. The only red in the picture is the end of her cigarette. She brings a touch of glamour to us.

'Hello,' I say.

Fiona re-crosses her legs at her ankles, flashing black court shoes and the sheen of expensive nylons, a prim position which doesn't suit the rest of her. She takes a drag and blows smoke into the room.

'You have grown, Jane. Quite the young lady. Your mother must be proud of you.'

I watch my mother wince. Mum isn't proud of me and she doesn't want me growing up.

'Let's see how she does with her exams,' is the way she cancels Fiona's compliment. 'You'll be applying for university next year, won't you? How did school go today?'

I look at my mother's smug expression and think, *you don't want to know, not really.*

'Today was fab.' At my slack sentence, Mum's lips tighten while Fiona's lips move towards a smile as she picks up on the discord between Mum and me. 'We had a debate.'

Mum pours tea, adding two spoonsful of sugar into hers. 'Tell us what the debate was about.'

Fiona doesn't take sugar.

I don't take tea. I won't be drinking it, not after I've finished.

'It was a topical subject,' I announce. 'My English teacher said I was a natural.'

Mum beams and suddenly I feel sorry for her. She can't win.

Fiona stops sipping. 'The motion was?'

I take a deep breath, feeling myself flush even before I say the words. In a clear voice, as if I'm announcing on the radio,

I repeat, 'That this house is in favour of sex before marriage.'

Mum chokes and clatters her cup back on its saucer. 'I've never heard of anything so ridiculous.'

Fiona takes a long, slow draw on her cigarette. 'Were you for or against?'

I open my mouth to answer but my mother's in first, her face pink, her eyes glancing about, neither fixing on me nor Fiona. 'Jane knows perfectly well what I think about that kind of talk.'

Half of me wishes I hadn't spoiled her afternoon but it's too late for regrets. I gamble that even Mum won't shut me up in front of her friend. 'Don't you want to know what I said, Mum?'

'Said?' Mum's pretence of good manners vanishes. She stares me out, her eyes glaring at me as if she wishes I'm not here. 'Said? About sex? At your age?' Her voice rises with each sentence. 'I'll tell you what you do about sex, Jane. You certainly don't debate it. You don't talk about it. You don't even think about it.'

It's the swinging sixties. I wonder about sex all the time.

Despite all my mother's little chats, and regardless of overheard night-time sounds from my parents' room, I knew nothing about sex, what happened between two people when they made love.

When I was thirteen, threatening Mum with the arrival of my period, she gave me her version of the facts of life, ending with, 'and then, well, you know…' and later, 'it's not something nice girls need worry about until their wedding night.'

'What did your mother say to you?' I asked.

'I didn't get a chance to ask her. With six children and her expecting again, I was seven years old when I was sent to live with my grandmother. Strict Baptist she was, with only the Bible to read on Sunday and certainly no hanging around in the street chatting to boys or any smutty talk.'

This was the first I'd heard of this and I was shocked. 'How long did you live with your grandmother?'

'Until I was fourteen. Old enough to work, to be a children's nanny, sleeping in the loft with the cold-water tank and rats running along the rafters.'

Which shut me up.

Now I wonder if my story could have turned out differently, if I could have found common ground with my mother over the growing up thing. But she was scared of me distancing myself from her influence, of what I might do to shame her, to ruin her plans to better herself.

I have a photo of my parents which sums them up totally. The naked trees show it was taken on a cold day in the back garden of our old house in Hertfordshire. They must have been about to go out somewhere because they are both dressed up. My father is wearing his weekend suit made of some kind of tweed complete with a waistcoat, his hair still dark and thick. He had a strong face with a Roman nose and liked to say he had French ancestors. My mother has on a flat fur hat, a heavy pancake squashing down on her head, and a suit with a tartan jacket I remember as green and black. She has her hands folded together across her black skirt and is simpering her I'm-looking-smart-expression, her smile of the lips pressed together. Neither of them appears to be overjoyed to be recorded in this way, but they do both look eminently respectable.

It wasn't all bad between my mother and me. I did try. On the first Sunday after moving to London, I went to church to keep her company. The church was on the main road, the bus route I would take to school. On the way we walked past the huge houses, with a bay window on the ground floor, iron steps leading to basements and more steps running up to the front door.

'Why can't we live in one of those houses,' I asked.

'They're probably split into flats,' she snapped. 'For people on national assistance.'

Two

As the old year of 1963 rolls out, it's Rita who takes me to my first London party.

My mother insists I must be home by eleven.

'Mu-u-m,' I plead. 'It's a New Year's Eve Party. I can't leave before midnight.'

My mother instructs me to bring Rita to meet her. I have to slip a note under her front door. I'd written, Mum wants to see you or I won't be able to come. Round about four this afternoon?

At four o'clock sharp, there's a ring on the front doorbell as if there's a fire in the road. I rush to open it, just to get over the shock of what Rita's wearing and how much makeup she has on. I gape at the unpainted face, the naked eyes and lips; the clean jeans and the aertex gym blouse.

Rita winks at me. 'Cup of tea then?'

In our breakfast room, my mother sits at her sewing machine.

'Rita's here Mum,' I say, as if this happens every day. 'I'll put the kettle on, shall I?'

My mother flutters her eyelashes at Rita and Rita smirks back. After twenty minutes of the smallest talk I have ever heard, 'We're doing A Midsummer Night's Dream and Jane's a brilliant Helena,' Rita pauses. 'Being tall and blonde.' Which floors my mother as she's never read Shakespeare.

'I am relying on you, Rita,' she says, 'to get Jane home safely by half-past twelve.'

Rita smirks. 'That's exactly what my mum'd like.'

As I open the front door for her I whisper, 'I owe you. See you Saturday.'

I wear a new shift dress I have made and sling-back shoes. I carry a shoulder bag, a present from my parents for my sixteenth birthday. There's enough time in the tube between leaving Balham underground station and arriving at Fulham for me to cover my shiny nose and the few spots on my chin with block face powder, draw a thin margin of dark brown eye-liner along my upper eyelids and fill in my lips with pale pink lipstick.

The party is in a house with tall, sash windows and a red front door. In the hall, a fir tree, decorated with baubles, lights and electric candles, reaches to the ceiling. Icons of riches and comfort. My mother would be pleased. There's a table, spread with a white cloth stacked with bottles and wooden boards of bread and cheese.

Rita mixes a vodka and orange. I pour a red vermouth. It's the drink my mother likes although she adds gin.

'See you later,' says Rita, twiddling her fingers at me, film-star style, and she's gone.

I sip my warm, red, sweet drink and listen to the Beatles sing Please, Please Me.

'Dance?' A boy with dark hair, holding a pint of beer in one hand and a cigarette in the other, stands before me. He winks at me as if we've met before.

Of course I'd like to dance. I nod.

He puts the cigarette between his lips so he can take my glass out of my hand and, with his, stands them on the mantelpiece.

After a twist, someone puts on Billy Fury's Halfway to Paradise. We stay dancing and I'm in paradise. He keeps smoking. I decide I like the scent and that it makes him sophisticated. When the record has stopped, we sit on a sofa. He says his name is Nick, I tell him mine. Nick isn't tall so he doesn't fit my mother's definition of a suitable boyfriend, but his hair flops across his forehead and over one eyebrow and, even in the night-time party light, I can see he has unusually dark blue eyes. I kind-of fancy him.

He leans towards me and kisses me, full on the lips but gently. I don't flinch but neither do I kiss him back. I've never had a boyfriend older than me and I'm not sure I want one. Are they all like Rita's blokes? When he suggests we go upstairs, I shake my head and take another drink. He shrugs, grins and lights up again and then the Beatles are screaming Twist and Shout and there's masses of dancing and masses of drinking, until I can't tell whether it's me whirling round or the room. He takes my hand to lead me upstairs to a double bed for masses of snogging. Which should make my party a success. I'm Cathy finding her Heathcliff, Scarlett O'Hara being overwhelmed by Rhett Butler. I might blush at the things he does but inside I'm glowing. My tongue has tasted tobacco on his and I'm cool with that. I'm enjoying the whole scene.

Until he says, 'Lose your virginity for me.'

I push him away and sit up, troubled and almost scared. This is suddenly all too grown up. I don't want to be part of Rita's world. Not yet. Maybe not ever. I scramble off the bed and search for the light. I don't look at Nick, just do up buttons and straighten stockings before running downstairs.

He calls after me, 'I'm not giving up.'

I make Rita leave with me just as the bells sound midnight.

I am not allowed to remain in my world of innocence. My mother won't let me. She will keep reminding me I have a choice. 'What did you do at the party, Jane?'

'Do?' I watch her pinning the seam on a new frock, same style, same Liberty fabric as all the rest, and am tempted to create havoc in her Garden of Eden, to say, I lost my virginity on a strange bed. But it wouldn't be true.

I wish I could talk to Mum about this, but I recall her edict on the afternoon Fiona visited and I daren't ask. Like a good girl I say, 'The music was great and the food.'

'Was there drink?'

'Beer and bitter lemon. That kind of stuff.'

'You behaved yourself?'

'Yes Mum.' Well, I did, didn't I? Considering what I could have done.

Since I can't talk to Mum, I rely on Rita.

On a freezing day in January, I join her for a fag behind the bike shed. Hardly anyone rides a bike to school these days so the wooden hut at the far end of the playground is abandoned.

Rita lights up and passes the cigarette to me. I suck, swallow, choke and hand it back.

She takes a smooth draw. 'You don't smoke do you?'

'I just wanted to get you out here.'

'Urgent is it?'

'Do you love your blokes?'

Rita laughs. 'Whatever gave you that idea?'

I colour, feeling stupid. 'Did you love the bloke you lost your virginity to?'

'He was a lorry driver and I was fourteen.'

'Fourteen?'

'I was broke and needed a lift home. Is this about Nick?'

I nod, miserable now that I have started this conversation. Because I can see where it is going to finish. With me admitting what a disaster I made of that party.

'Are you still a good girl?' Rita asks.

I feel myself colouring but don't reply.

'That's a yes?' She looks at me. 'If you're going to keep Nick, you'll have to give him what he wants. He's that kind.'

I refuse to be trapped. A sudden spurt of anger fires me up. 'I have no plans to see him ever again.'

After that conversation with Rita I felt very much the ignorant one. And also selfish. Perhaps, I argued with myself, I should have said yes to Nick. However, I was full of doubts. Would it hurt? Would my mother guess? At the back of my mind was a story I'd heard that you could always tell if a girl was a virgin by her eyes, although I hadn't a clue what it was about her eyes that gave her away. Did I, a teenager, have a clue what love meant? How many different kinds of love were there? Today, my naivety makes me want to weep.

What do I feel about Nick now? No warmth, certainly not love. Only a detachment as if he was from another life. The love I used to justify my actions, wasn't the kind of love a woman feels for her husband. Or possibly a lover. For me, an immature schoolgirl, it was romantic. Most of it.

Why did it all go so horribly wrong? What was so special about Nick that he changed me so completely, made me lie to my mother? Because I did lie. To meet him after school, I told Mother I was in the school play and promised to cook Sunday lunch. 'I'll do something special for you and Dad.' I was that devious.

From the day I met him at that party, through the cold and slush of January, the ice-cold winds of February, the change of tempo in March, to the showers of April, through the sweet blossoms of May and the fleeting warmth of June, I was Nick's girl. I protected him from my mother's cross-questioning by keeping him away from home. I relished Nick, chanting to myself, 'I have a boyfriend, I am going steady.' Hugged the secret of what we did together, in the half-light of the back row, to myself.

Nick told me he was nineteen going on twenty, had left school the previous summer and was working as a newspaper journalist. 'Financial. Researching figures, percentages, that kind of thing and then writing columns on it. Dead boring'.

I was impressed. 'That's just what I want to do. Not financial, of course, but write for a newspaper.'

'No, you don't, Janey. It's not that great. Look.' He pulled from his jacket pocket a magazine. Not a fun one like Honey, which I bought, but one printed in only two colours, black and red. Nick turned to an inside page and pointed to a square of print, boxed in with a black outline. The headline was, For Careful Investors. I scan read the lines, listing names of companies I'd never heard of with recommendations about their profits.

I thought, at least he might be good with money, and said, 'Well, that's something at least.' If I'd been honest with him, I'd have admitted I was disappointed. He was right. This cold prose was not how I saw journalism. But then he chucked the magazine to the ground and pulled me close to him, kissing me like no one had ever kissed me before. His tongue wasn't under control, but I didn't mind.

When he wasn't kissing me or unbuttoning me, he talked about himself. 'Once I have a bit of capital behind me I'm going into films.'

I couldn't see how Nick could suddenly move from newspapers to films, but the word capital was the kind of grown-up word my father used, and it pleased me. Forget schoolboys. I was going out with a man.

I have not forgotten, even if I can no longer conjure up, the magic of that first attraction; that fizzing feeling when a girl fancies a boy, wants a boy, even though she does not understand what it is she wants. Desire is such a grown-up emotion; surely the deep experience of sexual desire is only possible after you have made love, and more than once. It would be impossible to return to those early, girlish delights; those heady moments when lust first sweeps under a girl's skin.

The summer of 1964 is my summer of love. The common's our special place, the world of our secret meetings. The weather is kind to us and the swathes of London brushwood offer us privacy from the little kids with their mums and the teenage boys desperate for a quick fag. Lying under the lilac tree in May or inhaling the sweet white scent of a mock orange in June, I make my own heaven of cool grass, warm touches and hot yearnings. Nick's mouth tastes sweet from the cola he's drunk and sour from the cigarettes he smoked. By five past four his tainted fingers are inside my dress, undoing my bra hooks. The afternoon sun tarnishes my hair gold, warms my uncovered breasts.

'My two albino cherries,' Nick whispers. 'Small and perfectly sweet.'

Nick's energetic male smell excites me, and my body does its best to match his damp patches and intimate trickles. The grass tickles the backs of my knees and the rims of my ears. High above us, a plane hums its song of getting away from it all. The light behind my lids is purple with yellow flashes and, no, I'm not on anything except the highway to love.

One escapade which encapsulates that false freedom I'm feeling is a day of sun and sea and not quite sex.

It's July, the weather already hot. After assembly, our headmistress delivers a homily about skipping school. In her thick heeled shoes with round toes and a pattern of holes punched on top with a little bow, she stands erect, her folded arms making a padded shelf for her huge bosom. Rita sighs and raises her eyes to the heaven she hasn't been praying to. 'We're getting out of this place,' she whispers.

In the cloakroom, she changes out of her navy skirt and cardigan into a pair of denims and a T-shirt. Glancing at my summer uniform, a shift dress in a vague blue and white flowery pattern, she shrugs. 'They're waiting.'

'Who are?'

'Your Nick and that friend of his called Les. With his car.'

'Nick!' My heart races with pleasure, my head bursting with yellow happiness. I'm about to play truant from school.

Parked in the road is a green Mini. When he sees us, Nick jumps out and holds open the door. 'Janey, in the back with me. Rita sit next to Les and show him the way.'

The car smells of flat beer and cigarettes. Nick pulls up his legs, hugging his knees and grinning at me as if he's still a schoolboy himself. 'We're going to the seaside.' He kisses me on my cheek. 'Brighton beckons.'

'No work?' I can't help saying.

'Friday's a quiet day.'

Les revs the car and we whip around the corner and onto the road running across Clapham Common. The madness of it all makes my pulse tick under the skin of my wrist, my heart beat faster, as fast as Les is driving the car. The fact I'm not supposed to be anywhere near a car, that I'm doing things I've never done, makes me feel daring and reckless.

Les winds down the windows and turns up the radio. It's only skiffle music but it sounds jazzy, glamorous. The notes of the electric guitars dance across the pavement, loud enough to make a woman sweeping her steps stop to watch us as we race past her gate, the breeze we create messing with her neat little pile of dirt. We laugh and wave, not caring that her scowl means we're already behaving badly.

The drive to Brighton passes in a melody of swapped jokes and smutty remarks as Les chats up Rita. I let my body roll against Nick's while he kisses the rim of my ear and runs his hand up my leg until I tell him to stop.

We reach the town. Les parks not far from the front, and we uncurl ourselves, stretch and walk The Lanes, wander the promenade. Giggling, with my arms around Nick in a couldn't-care-less way, I stare at cheeky postcards of men in too tight trousers, their faces pink with sexy thoughts, leering at fat ladies.

I buy a hat with Kiss Me Quick written on it and race along the front, Nick chasing me until he catches me and kisses me, tongues and all. I hand over the money for a stick of rock with A Present from Brighton stamped through it, take one bite before passing it to Rita, who crunches it hard enough to chip a tooth before chucking it to Les who finishes it. The sea breeze whips candy floss into my face, covering my lips and nose with the livid pink stickiness of the stuff. We eat chips to stave off hunger and an ice cream to quench our thirst.

Finally, we make for the beach, with its family groups, mums handing out sandwiches, which you know from bitter childhood experience are full of sand, the chocolate bourbons which are soft and the bottles of coke which are warm.

The four of us settle down on the sand, not interested in the sea or the sandcastles, only in who will make the first move, to lie back, pretending to sunbathe (Nick) and then who'll be the second one (Rita). I beat Les to the next move, showing I'm prepared to make a couple by lying close to Nick and drawing him into a cuddle and then into a kiss and then a snog not caring who sees or who minds.

A Girl Guide troop spread rugs on the sand, the captain handing out packed lunches.

By now my dress is rucked up to my thighs but I don't care. I'm pretending to be bold, to be with it, to show those goody Girl Guides what they could enjoy if they let themselves.

'Do you have to behave like this on the beach?' A woman's voice booms over us. The Guide captain's thick body casts a shadow. 'Some of my Guides are only twelve.'

Nick pulls away from me, leaving me splayed, my body exposed more intimately than if I'd been wearing a swimsuit. I sit up, pulling down my dress and looking anywhere else than at the Guides who are giggling and making me feel silly rather than sophisticated.

Nick quickly takes over. 'I do apologize. I thought this part of the beach was empty.' Talking just as my father might. 'It's so easy to get carried away. It's the sun. Much too good to waste.' He smiles his best-boy smile. 'Sorry if we've been a nuisance.' To us he snarls, 'Get up you lot. Time to go.'

I wished I hadn't made a fool of myself. I was ashamed. I should have behaved like my mother's daughter and not made an exhibition of myself. I was angry with Nick who, by implying it was my fault, that I'd seduced him into the day, had belittled me instead of protecting me. Why hadn't I reclaimed my self-respect and chucked him? It would have saved both my mother and me a great deal of trouble and heartache.

By the time we reach London it's raining. Sitting at traffic lights, I stare at a couple of hydrangea bushes planted in a front garden. The rain's watering them, cleaning them, as I wish it could clean me. Pearls of water roll across the leaves of the shrub. The blue-pink petals remind me of bad-taste bathing caps disguised with rubber curls.

Les drops me at the end of Emmanuel Road. Rushing in, I don't have time to change. I can smell stale sweat under my dress and feel sand in my shoes, a token of childhood.

'That you, Jane?' My mother's voice from the breakfast room, where she's at her sewing machine.

'Bit late. Had to go to the library.' *Guilty*, says the gremlin in my head. *Guilty as hell.*

Pictures of those hours at Brighton sit with the gremlin. Blue sea. Pebble beach. Red and white deck chairs. Pink rock. An illustration from a child's book.

I long to be able to confide in my mother, to share confidences, tell her I was in love.

'If only you could have seen us,' I'd say. 'Larking along the promenade, chasing each other. It's great being a teenager. D'you remember?'

But she doesn't. I know enough about my mother's life to understand she never knew. One minute she was a little girl, the next she was caring for a little brother or two or three. My mother wouldn't understand no matter what I tell her.

I remember reading an article in the Sunday paper. I was lying on my stomach on the sitting room carpet, the pages spread out before me.

Mum came in and glanced down at the headline. The Pill free on NHS.

Her voice shattered the weekend calm, a stone breaking clear glass. 'If I ever find those things in your handbag, I'll beat the living daylights out of you.'

I didn't bother pointing out that the only clinic which prescribed contraceptives to unmarried girls was in Birmingham. I wasn't even sure where Birmingham was.

I return to my photo album, to one of the last photos I took before I stopped keeping pictures which look innocent but do not tell the whole truth.

There he is: on the common, his back curved, his head jutting out slightly, his hair long enough to cover the tops of his ears, legs crossed beneath him. In his right hand he has a cigarette, his eyes half-closed against the smoke. To me, now, he looks aloof, distant. Maybe he was, and I just didn't see it. In my girlish way, I thought Nick's attitude was poetic, cool as we used to say.

Nick. The person who shared my betrayal of my mother, making my life a web of secrets. Those afternoons, dedicated to kissing, cuddling and touching, full of denied desire were very much a thing of the sixties.

Had I loved Nick? According to my mother, love was for adults, for the over twenty-ones. But love is the only way I can explain the effect Nick had on me. I loved being with him, loved hearing him talk, watching him smoke, looking at his hands knowing that when the fag was finished Nick would stub it out on the grass, push me down and undo the buttons on the front of my dress. And I loved all that followed. I loved him to touch me, to make ripples run under my flesh, to stroke my legs and melt away my thighs, to kiss me again and again.

◆ ◆ ◆

Among my pile of papers, a page written with an Italic nib and brown ink, catches my eye. A letter.

> *And what would you say now if I said, 'Come to bed with me'? You'd say 'No!' The question is, why would you say 'No'. The best would be because it's safer baby-wise, secondly it would go against everything your parents have said and lastly because you probably consider it wrong morally. But if you said, 'Yes,' heavens knows what I would do. So far all I have done is talked about going to bed with you.*
>
> *All my fondest love, Nick*

I have to smile. This letter makes him sound caring. Which he was at first. I read it twice, the irony of the words amusing me.

Three

That autumn, Nick's frequent letters, always written in brown ink, delighted me.

22 October 1964
My darling Janey,

How are you? Glad you have a Saturday job although you're worth more than a pound a day. I can just see you advising old dears on what to wear for Christmas.

I love you with every beat of my heart and will always be there for you and look after you, I will always be by your side.

Nick xxx

It's a Saturday evening in early December. As we cross the common I put a hand on Nick's arm, turning him towards me. 'I need to talk to you.'

'What is it?' he says.

Which isn't encouraging. 'I've missed September, October and November.'

He walks me quickly to a bench by an old public lavatory. We sit down.

'Christ, Jane, why didn't you say before?'

'In October I thought my dates might have changed a bit. By November I hoped I might be wrong. But now I've missed again, so I must be right.'

'I'm taking you to a doctor. Don't say a word until you're sure.'

I know for sure. I should be looking forward to Christmas, to Mum and Dad being full of good cheer, maybe to Nick coming over with presents. The only present I want is blood in my knickers.

Standing outside school, I push my hands into the pockets of my coat and pull the hood round my face, knowing how uncomfortable Shakespeare's Marion felt with her red and raw nose. The December morning has a clear baby blue sky, promising a night freeze.

I hear a smooth-sounding engine. I glance at my watch. Ten thirty. Just as he promised. My spirits lift at this evidence of reliability but I'm shocked by the car which stops beside me, a shiny grey limousine. The driver is wearing a chauffeur's uniform. My life is turning into a ridiculous charade.

The rear door opens and Nick says. 'I told you I'd get a good car.'

Which seems daft to me. Here we are with nothing between us but a great black cloud of fear and Nick's wasting money on a grand gesture. Nick with his dark floppy hair and his grin. I soften, my objections to his wasted money washed away by his smile.

Inside the car, with the partition between us and the driver pulled across, I let Nick unbutton my coat and pat my tummy. 'How are we in there?'

The car glides, a chariot on an ice road which is about to crack. His easy humour aggravates me. 'I thought you want me to be wrong?' Any minute now I might feel that familiar dampness, that telling way the crotch of my pants sticks to my body. I'd welcome the mess, the cramps, the nuisance of it all.

I move away from him, pull down the armrest and we sit, surrounded by hired leather. We drive through Brixton, up to the Elephant and Castle, crossing the river over Tower Bridge, all the time thinking how silly this is, me in my school uniform, riding in a chauffeur driven car. It should be my wedding day. But do I want to marry him? Do I want Nick for my ever-after husband? I make a joke of it all. 'I plan to ride in a limo on my wedding day.'

Which is met with silence.

Stupidly I persist. The devil is driving me to dig my own grave. 'But it isn't my wedding day, is it?' My voice wobbles, watery. 'I'm in a limo all right but I'm not in white; I haven't even got a ring. I'm doing things in the wrong order.' I sound like my mother but not nearly as much as Nick does.

'Bit late to think of that now.' His voice is cold and unloving.

My mother's will be cold and full of righteous anger. A stone settles in my chest, but I ignore it and tell myself it's going to be all right. After all, what can happen to me? They can't send me to prison.

Taking a right onto the Whitechapel Road, the car picks up speed. It's a straight run then to the East End. The car's going fast now, quickly carrying me to the truth. As the names flash by, Stepney Green, Mile End, Stratford and onto Leytonstone, I shiver. My next chat with my mother will be less than cosy. It will be a crucifixion.

I begin to have a quick little chat with Him-up-There even though I know I don't deserve one.

Dear God, please don't let me be pregnant. I promise I'll give Nick up. I'll do my school work. I'll do anything. Just as long as it's all right.

It's a prayer too late. God must hear that prayer from schoolgirls every day of the week. He must be bored stiff by prayers like that. He must think, *I didn't make you pregnant. You got yourself in this mess, keep your prayers to yourself.*

Doctor Mason is young, fair with soft cheeks. He looks as though he ought to be smiling but isn't. After saying hello to Nick, he points to a curtain pulled back to show a headless bed, a brown plastic mattress with a white sheet on it. He turns to me. 'Take off your knickers and lie down on the couch.' He sounds cold, uncaring.

It was only after he's pulled the curtains across, more brown but with a border of yellow sunflowers nodding at me like a cluster of maternal Little Weeds, I realise he didn't say Hello.

I put my bag under the chair, pulled off my pants, a pathetic white scrap of a shield between me and transgression, and drop them on top of my duffle coat. I climb on the couch and lie back. On the other side of the curtain, water's running. There's the sloop of soap being squirted from one of those dispensers and then the slurp of hands washing each other.

When the doctor lifts the curtain, I'm lying stiffly straight, my skirt over my knees, my feet together. Too late I see I am still wearing my short, white socks. The pair of turned down tops make me feel worse than naked; the childish garments declare me too juvenile for sex, let alone pregnancy.

'Right then. Let's have a look.' His voice is curt when I needed kind. Impersonal when I long for personal. Efficient when I desire warmth. He pushes my skirt up and my knees apart.

I look down at myself and am ashamed. No man has seen me like this before. Even Nick has not stared up between my legs, at my most private places, as if they are diagrams in a medical textbook.

The doctor puts his hand on my tummy and presses. His skin is cold. He glances up at me, frowning. He presses harder, the heel of his hand just above my pubic bone. My abdomen's full. Then I realise it's not just a look he needs but a feel. His fingers probe. I wince. Twice. He pushes inside me, hurting me just enough to imply, This is only a foretaste of what's to come, and he still isn't smiling. He straightens up and leaves.

The news has to be bad. If not, he'd have smiled and said, nothing to worry about.

He returns carrying a small, clear, plastic envelope. 'Here are two pills. Take one today and one in two days' time. If you're not pregnant, you'll come on.'

I'm still lying half-naked. I tug at my skirt. 'If I am?'

'The pills won't have any effect. Your baby won't be hurt.'

'Can't you…?' but I don't know how to say what I want.

After the doctor has gone, turning his back on me and my troubles, I put my feet on the lino and stand up. My legs are shaking and, in spite of the radiator against the wall, I'm shivering. I twist my knickers in a muddle. I can hear Doctor Mason talking to Nick. I know I might as well throw away the pills.

Because the doctor's saying, 'Don't expect her parents to be delighted.'

I swallow those little red pills the doctor gave me. My knickers stay as whitely pristine as the frost on the lawn. The only smudge of pink is on the horizon where, at eight in the morning, the sun struggles to convince me to get up. I almost blurt it out to Mum, saying, please don't be cross with me. It wasn't meant to happen. I've been trying to tell you for ages.

Who am I kidding? She's a domestic science teacher, not only caring how I behave but quite clear about what I am supposed to be. Which is to be a good girl, come up with a set of A levels to get me into university and to make them proud of me on my graduation day. None of which I am or can ever be. Not now.

When I wake, there's this thing with me. It isn't a cloud above my head. Nothing so routine. Neither a void beneath me. Nothing so empty. Nor a heaviness within me. Nothing so tangible. It's a creature from a hitherto foreign world; a growth I do not want to nurture, grinding me down, crushing out of me my fun in living, my youth, my right even to exist. I'm afraid of what it might do to me. I loathe it, yet for just a second, on waking in the morning, I can't remember what it is. And then I can. I'm pregnant.

17 December
Last day of term. Really odd. Rita wishes me the best of luck. Her parting words are, 'You'll be OK.'

Mum's in the kitchen, peeling potatoes. I take over while she pulls down cookery books, opens them, glances through them and then piles them up, still open, on the kitchen table.

'What are you doing?'

'Looking for a different way of cooking turkey. And a fresh recipe for the pudding. What about the cake? I like the traditional way with plenty of marzipan and icing but Fiona might not? What do you think?'

My stomach heaves. I peel a few more spuds. Mashed potato is one thing I can eat without feeling sick. 'What's all this for?'

'Christmas is almost here, Jane.'

As if I don't know. My timing couldn't be worse. Christmas, a time of peace and joy and I am about to turn it into a... what? Maybe, just maybe, Mum will see things my way. After all, isn't Christmas all about a baby born to an unmarried woman and doesn't every woman love a baby?

I try, 'I wouldn't overdo it. Not for the three of us.'

'I'm inviting Fiona for the twenty-fifth.'

'Fiona? On Christmas Day?'

'Why not.'

'She's hardly the Virgin Mary.'

Mum tips potatoes into a saucepan. 'Fiona likes seeing you and hearing how well you are doing at school. Besides, I need her opinion about which university you should apply for.'

I must rescue my mother from her false fantasies. The next day, as soon as she leaves to shop for her festive day, I dial Nick's number. My heart is thudding but not from the joy of being about to speak to him. My mouth is dry. I am afraid. The phone is picked up by his Ma.

I have to clear my throat. 'Can I speak to Nick please?' I sound so squeaky clean, so timid.

Her response is quick. 'He's not here.'

'When will he be back?'

'Don't ask me.'

Any optimism I have vanishes. 'In the pub?' I ask.

Her voice turns nasty. 'What do you expect, when you've landed him in this mess?'

I feel sick. I try to speak. Try. I have no words. He's told her. His mother knows about my pregnancy before my own mother does. I almost hate him, except I can't. He's the father of my baby. I slam the phone down.

When Nick finally rings me, we're watching a play on the BBC. Quickly, I say, 'I'll get it.'

And feel a surge of relief as I hear his voice. 'It's me, Jane. What did you want?'

I have to be quick. 'When are you coming over? We can hardly leave it until I'm in a maternity smock.'

'OK, OK, I get the message. Look Jane are you sure this is going to work?'

My heart plummets. He doesn't want me, not in a married way. Not in a mummy and daddy and sweet little baby makes three way. My sickness churns and I want to cry. I take a deep breath. 'We have to do it before the twenty-fifth.'

I should cut loose, tell him I'll manage on my own. But I'm having his baby and it won't go away just because my choice of boyfriend is another thing I've got wrong. I know I sound desperate but I say, 'You will come, won't you?'

'Of course I will Janey.'

But he doesn't say he loves me. I put down the receiver and bite back the tears. If Mum sees tears she'll guess something is very wrong.

'I'll come over on the twenty-fourth.' He'd sounded defeated.

The pudding is made and boiling happily in Mum's largest saucepan. The turkey is sitting in the fridge and the cake is iced. In the lounge, the tree is dressed, the tinsel and the lights twinkling, although in the blue light of a winter morning, it looks strangely out of place, as if we have the wrong month. Caught out by the weather plunging us into a sub-zero world, my father has turned up the boiler in the kitchen and lit the fire in the lounge but even the flames are the wrong colour, much too yellow to create any warmth. A bottle of sherry and four glasses sit on the coffee table as if we are about to play Happy Families. Only I suspect the game will end up as Murder in the Dark.

Nick turns up on time and I breathe relief all over him. But he doesn't kiss me. His bleak expression warns me it isn't only my parents who are going to be tricky. I tell myself the baby is here to stay and we'll all make the best out of a bad situation.

I shut the lounge door, sealing the two of us in.

Nick looks grim. 'What happens?'

'We ask their permission.'

Nick sniggers. 'Bit late for that.'

He's behaving like a child. I suspect he's scared. I must be patient with him. 'For permission to get married. I'm under age, remember?'

The door opens and Mum, dressed in a wool dress with three-quarter sleeves and wearing her pearls, looking like the Queen giving her Christmas message, is all smiles. 'How are you Nick?'

Nick mumbles something I can't decipher.

Dad joins us and asks Nick if he'd like a sherry. We stand in silence as my father hands the glasses over. I gulp mine. The quicker it's all over the better. I take a deep breath. 'We've got something to tell you.'

'What's this all about?' My mother settles herself on the settee sipping and smiling.

I huddle back into the armchair in front of the window. I read somewhere that sitting with the light behind you makes you look younger. If I look vulnerable I might be forgiven. Nick moves to stand beside the chair, one hand on my shoulder as if we're posing for a *Country Life* portrait. I know my expression is unaccountably glum. 'There's something we want to talk to you about,' I say.

My mother giggles and flushes with excitement and it hits me she's expecting us to announce our engagement. I'm irritated by her romantic take on the scene. I'm still at school. Not only am I not about to get engaged, I'm having a baby. I remember Rita's advice, back in the school library, the day she produced that tablet. Take it while you've got the chance.

Now, Nick is my best chance. I reach up and across the back of the chair, my fingertips searching for his.

Nick clears his throat. 'Jane and I would like to get married.'

My father is standing with his back to the fireplace, hands behind his back, his Duke of Edinburgh persona round him like a cloak. He coughs.

I'm reminded of that stage in a bullfight where the bull paws the ground as if testing to see if it will bear his weight. With measured words, he speaks. I'm too nervous to understand joined-up sentences; I hear his words in disjointed phrases.

'…still at school … A levels to do … hoping she'd go to university…'

Feeling my face flush, giving me away, I glance across to Mum, who's watching me, her face taught. Her voice is not of a doting grandmother or even loving mother, but of a wicked stepmother. 'Why?'

At last I say it. 'I'm pregnant.'

'Jane is expecting our child.'

Nick and I speak together betraying we are not in unison. His words have made me sound like the Virgin Mary. If I had the nerve I'd joke about foolish virgins but it's as well I don't because my mother uses the same word but in a totally demeaning way.

'You little fool.'

Her voice is a knife slicing through me. Any guts I have abandon my body leaving me with a huge chasm of desperation.

My father rounds on Nick, standing in front of him, challenging him. 'You despicable little piece of shit.' His voice is strong, his face a livid red. 'I'd like to horsewhip you.' His fists clench and unclench. Small movements, impossible to ignore. But he doesn't move, not take one step towards his victim. His anger might transport him to a world of hangings and floggings but it's a world he can't act out.

I sense Nick tremble and know he's a coward. I also know I don't want to marry him.

His voice is thin, using weak words. 'We love each other. We want this child.' He's summarizing every girl's dream: to be loved and to be having a baby. But his words, spoken as if he's steeped himself in Bible talk, kills any love I've ever felt for him.

Suddenly, my mother has the presence of mind to be practical. 'How do you know? Are you sure?' Her optimism, that I'd made a mistake, stings me more than her calling me a fool. Hers is a hopeless wish, a stretching out for the impossible. No one will grant me a miracle now.

41

I stare into those blinking eyes. 'I've been to a doctor.'

The blinking becomes faster as if she can't credit anything I tell her. 'When?'

'About two weeks ago,' I say. 'To a doctor Nick knows.'

'What did this doctor say, exactly?'

I make the mistake of shrugging.

'Don't you act dumb insolence with me, my girl.' Mum's teeth clench behind bitten lips.

'He said I was pregnant.' I look at my father, at the man who sat me on his knee when I was little and watched over me when I was brave enough to swim in the sea. Seeing those scenes in a flash, I can't believe I've lost that man with a few words. 'Dad, don't be angry with me.'

He's staring at Nick as if he were the devil incarnate. 'I'd like to thrash the living daylights out of you.'

Nick takes a step forward. 'If you want a fight, fine by me.'

'Outside.' My father snatches at the door handle and pulls it open.

I almost laugh. The idea of them fighting, actually punching each other in the back garden, it's a scene from a B movie.

Shadows are flickering across Nick's face. I'm in no doubt he's in his worst nightmare. The two men storm out of the room, through the kitchen and into the back garden.

I beg Mum to stop them but she's blinking at me as if she can make me disappear like pictures in a book when you flip the pages over. Her lips roll and unroll as if they can't decide whether to speak or keep quiet. As she takes a deep breath, I wonder if she's going to ask how I've been, as in sick or not, or maybe she's just a little bit sorry for me, being caught out like this. Maybe her breezy side will come to my rescue and she'll say, 'There's nothing to be done about it but to look for the bright side.'

As we hear the back door banging, she whispers, 'If you'd cut me up in little pieces you couldn't have hurt me more.'

No tears or cuddling, no helpful words or loving gestures.

I take refuge in her word hurt. Maybe if she's hurt, she might imagine how sad I am. Sad at losing my way over this and, yes, sad at hurting my mum, sad at angering my dad.

'How far gone are you?' She stares at me as if defying me to know the answer.

My heart gives a small skip and bright yellow flickers in my head. Mum is at least interested in what stage I've reached. She does care. 'Three months,' I begin. 'We went to a doctor. He couldn't be certain, but I know because I know when I fell…'

But my mother isn't looking the least bit like a mother listening to her daughter telling her about one of the greatest moments of her life, she's not even doing her blinking any more. Her eyes are steady, her voice, forced. 'You should have come to me earlier.'

Which lost me.

'If you'd told me when you first suspected, we could have done something about it.'

I experience a horror I've never known before, more than the fright of knowing I'm pregnant. Pregnant is at least legal. I have to be sure what she was prepared to do to save herself, to save her reputation. For I know it is herself she would have been saving, not me. 'I don't understand.'

43

'Gin. Hot baths. Your father's mother got rid of one with knitting needles.'

Irritation, anger, nervousness, fear, they all become revulsion. 'You'd have done that to me?'

'I'd have done anything.' She adds, 'Maybe we still can.'

The air in the room turns cold, solid, blocking me in. I'm being dragged along by an ice-drift, pulled down by a glacier. I'm more than numb, I'm isolated, totally alone at some distant pole where no one has been before me. My mother, the one person who is supposed to love me, is supposed to be close to me, to protect me against marauders, wants to stick sharp steel in my baby, twist and gouge until my baby and my wasted innards become the same bloody mess on the floor. To risk killing me.

A small icicle is thawed by truth. 'It's too late.'

'How can you be sure?'

I don't tell her about Rita's large, cream tablet with the brown powder. I have the feeling she'd rush round the corner to Rita's house and demand some more. But I do tell her about the doctor's small red ones. 'Nothing happened.'

Suddenly, shouting, 'We must stop them,' my mother runs from the room and into the kitchen, calling, 'Gerald. Come back inside. We don't want the neighbours to know.'

Reality broke horror into a million clips of truth. I'd forgotten the neighbours. Key players in this drama even though we have little to do with them. Whatever else happens, they must believe that the script we rely on in our house is that of Happy Families. I run after my mother to confront the men. No black eyes. Just my father looking smug. Nick, looking shifty, walks past me without a word and into the hall.

'He's leaving.' My father makes the statement as if it explains everything. He turns to me. 'As for you, no decent man will ever want you.'

'But…' I begin. I was expecting Mum to be difficult but Dad had always been so kind to me, indulgent even. Aren't fathers supposed to adore their daughters? I'd turned his love for me sour. I needed Nick, he was all I had, and he was walking away from me.

'When shall I see you…?' I run along the hall to stop Nick who already has his hand on the door latch but my mother lunges at my arm, dragging me back, holding me still.

'You don't see him. Not anymore.' She nods towards Nick. 'Get out. We'll look after our daughter.'

Nick opens the front door and walks out of the house.

My mother's voice is too close. 'I never dreamt my daughter would become a slut.'

I'm not surprised at her vile language. Maybe she's nearer the truth than I care to admit. Certainly, I have no idea how the rest of the world will treat me or my baby. I appeal to her once more. 'What's going to happen now?'

'Your father and I will decide what is going to happen to you and that…' she struggles for a moment, 'thing inside you.' She swoops towards me, her face distorted. 'A fine Christmas present you've given me.'

I retreat to my room. In the middle of the floor is a woman's magazine. I flick it open, to discover a feature entitled Christmas – A Family Occasion. I laugh out loud before letting the magazine slide to the floor. I lie on the carpet and list the facts in my head.

One, I'm pregnant. Two, I've told my mother. Three, she hates me. Four, Nick has gone. Five, he doesn't love me. Six, I don't want to marry him. Not anymore. At best he can't stand up for me. At worst he's a coward. Do I really want to chain myself to him for the rest of my life? But number seven on my list is that the baby is his as well as mine and will arrive despite us. Eight tells me, for the sake of our baby, I have to marry him. A tear rolls down my cheek. I lick and taste salt water. The first drop of an ocean. Screwing up my eyes I hate parents and knitting needles and tablets of all kinds. And boyfriends.

I climb on my bed and lie back, my eyes closed, one hand on my abdomen. He's in there, my baby, within my body, safe from the cruel world. I have about six months to find a place to take him. Somehow, I have to create a world for us, a world where he'll be loved, by me and with me. I close my eyes. In the secret folds of my mind, in the centre of my heart, I begin to love my baby.

Christmas is cancelled. My mother telephones Fiona, explaining she's decorating and the house is in a muddle. No one troubles to switch on the tree lights and, although we eat turkey, the three of us only speak when necessary. On Boxing Day my mother clears the presents from under the tree with the words, 'All ready to give away at next year's children's service.'

I am an outcast and, while my parents watch television, I steal slices of cake, rich with marzipan and royal icing, from the tin.

Four

YOUR FIRST GRANDCHILD –
DREAD OR DELIGHT?

The headline in my daily paper summarised my mother's very middle-class dilemma in six words. Only the emphasis was different. The latest fear peddled in the press was that women didn't want to accept their age, or their role in the family, especially as a grandmother. My mother's dilemma was that she wanted grandchildren but not before her daughter was wed, not before she'd seen her daughter walk down the aisle in a long, white frock while the organ played a jubilant tune.

I knew she longed for grandchildren. In fact, before she died, she insisted life wasn't fair because she only had four grandchildren whereas a friend of hers had been blessed with seven. I almost said, You certainly didn't want the first one, but refrained. She was old and suffering from dementia. I couldn't be that cruel.

Thursday 7 January 1965
First day of term. Dad rang school to say I have a
health problem! Mum is not at work.

47

The winter sun is shining, determined not to give in to seasonal expectations. I go down to breakfast as if nothing has changed. My mother asks me if I'd like cornflakes.

'Just tea, thank you.'

She pours a cup for me and one for herself, sipping it slowly, sighing between swallowing to let me know she's still thinking about it all.

When I can bear her silence no longer, I ask, 'What happens now?'

My mother puts down her cup. 'What happens now is that you do as you're told while I take steps to sort out this mess you've landed me in.'

I open my mouth to point out that it's me in the mess, but she holds up her hand.

'Don't argue with me. You and that miserable little toad have put your father and me in the most embarrassing and shameful situation. There must be a way of saving our reputation and I intend to find it.' She finishes her tea and replaces the cup on its saucer with enough venom to poison half the reptile house at London Zoo. 'First,' she tells me, 'I need to be sure you're telling me the truth.'

I'm flabbergasted. 'Why would I lie?'

'Don't take that rude tone with me, Jane. I have to make absolutely sure you and Nick are not…'

'Making it all up? Is that what we are to you? Two kids playing at mothers and fathers?'

'I trusted you and you let me down. I'm taking you to our doctor. Tomorrow.'

The next morning there's a slow drizzle, as though the rain understands exactly how I feel.

'I suppose you knew what you were doing?' Mum asks as we walk to the doctor's.

'What exactly do you mean?' I'm as rebellious as I sound.

'Was he putting it in the right place?'

I stamp a foot through a shallow puddle. 'For God's sake, Mum.'

'I'm your mother. I have to ask things like that.'

'All this doctor stuff is totally unnecessary. The last thing I want is that slimy old man pawing me up.'

The surgery is on the ground floor of a tall house on the main road. The front door is opened by the receptionist. The buttons on her white nylon overall strain across her chest, hinting at a shocking-pink bra. Inside, the hall is painted brown, the lino on the floor is cracked and curls up in the corners. Against the yellowing cornices, cobwebs nestle.

In his room, Doctor Seers pats my arm. 'How are you?'

I shift out of reach. 'Pregnant.'

'That's nothing new. Lots of girls…' he turns to my mother, 'You're upset, my dear.'

Mum's voice is her crisp one. 'That's putting it mildly.'

'Jane, I'll have to examine you. Shall we ask your mother to wait outside?'

'Whatever she likes.'

It seems my mother is beginning to feel protective towards me, because she asks, 'Will you be all right?'

He rubs his hands together. 'You leave her with me for a couple of minutes. Dee will make coffee.'

When it's all over, I remain on the surgical couch covered with a white sheet, indulging in a final hope that the sight of me, weak and vulnerable, might win my mother round.

Until the doctor rings through to the receptionist for a list of antenatal clinics.

My mother returns clutching a manila folder to her chest, blinking as if she could blink away the sins of the world.

Dr Seers puts his arm around her. 'Let's have a little chat.' He pauses before he confirms the news. 'Jane is about seventeen weeks pregnant. Maybe a little more. That makes delivery due around the middle of June.' He lets go of my mother who sits down heavily. He settles behind his desk, once more the detached medical man, and opens the folder. 'I'll write you a referral letter, Jane, to take to the antenatal clinic either at St Thomas's or St James's.'

My mother jumps up as if she can't just sit there while I'm allowed to be pregnant. 'I'm sure it's not as late as that. Couldn't you…' But she falters.

He closes the folder and gives her a long, cold stare. 'Your daughter is definitely pregnant. I suggest you put any thoughts like that out of your head.'

My mother looks ashamed and I almost feel sorry for her. We wait, my mother and I, a thousand unsaid words between us, as the doctor writes a short letter, folds it into an envelope, seals and addresses it before handing it to me.

My mother has had enough of this pretence that everything's fine, that life is wrapped in baby paper with ribbon round it. 'I'll have that.'

Dr Seers ignores her. 'This is yours, Jane. As soon as you can, book your confinement.'

I stuff the letter into my duffle coat pocket. 'Can we go now?' My voice is thin, and I realise I am shocked by my condition being confirmed from someone in my mother's world.

As I follow her from his surgery, he takes my arm and pulls me back. It seems the doctor has one last piece of advice as he whispers to me, 'When this is all over come back and see me again. It's a great pity you didn't come earlier.' Then he reaches out and touches me on my hip.

Outside it has stopped raining. The sun is doing its best to turn the day into one of those bright days which brings everyone out of doors to exercise off the Christmas pudding.

As we walk slowly along the pavement, a great sadness engulfs me. All this talk of clinics and confinements should have been a joyous occasion, a time of bringing mother and daughter closer, a time of sharing hopes and fears, joys and worries. But it can't be. No matter how I look at it, my mother and I are at war.

She asks, 'He examined you then?'

'Yes.'

'And gave you a date?'

'You heard. Somewhere around the middle of June.'

'What did he mean? That bit about going back after it was all over?'

'He's got to be joking. I'm not going back to him, not ever.'

'Why did he say it was a pity you didn't see him earlier? Earlier than what?'

I don't answer for a moment. My mother's dealing with enough. But a certain kind of triumph wins the moment. 'He said our conversation was confidential.'

'Confidential? Jane, we've months of not falling out, trying to get on with each other while we wait. You're not as grown up as you think, or you wouldn't be pregnant.'

Her crisp tone of voice gives her away. My mum does not care about me one jot.

I stop walking and turn to face her. She flinches. Maybe I look as desperate as I am. My mouth works for a second or two, fighting, but finally I tell her. 'You're dead right,' I say. 'I wouldn't be pregnant. Because do you know what that nice doctor said to me?'

'He shouldn't have spoken to you without me being there. You're still a minor.'

'His very words were, You should have come to me, my dear. I know what you girls are like. At your age it's all you think about. I could have given you something to keep you safe. We could have come to some arrangement.' I pause, gulp and clench my hands. When I open my mouth, it is to scream at my mother, my voice high, rasping, nothing like the voice of a young girl. 'Is that what you want to hear? How grown-up I could have been? Visiting that seedy man for contraceptive pills in exchange for a bit of illicit pawing and fingering? Is that what I should have done? To save your reputation?'

My mother takes hold of my arm and marches me along the pavement, around the corner into Emmanuel Road, across it and through our gate. She has to let go of me to find her front door key and open up, but then she reaches for me and thrusts me inside.

It's a bright, brisk January day, the grass in the back garden sprinkled with frost. The second week of term and I'm back at school.

My mother has insisted on me seeing my headmistress. 'She should know what is going on in her school.'

'I'm not going.'

'You are. It will bring it home to you what you are putting us all through.'

I follow my mother along the corridor towards Miss Beale's study, hoping I'd catch a glimpse of Rita, to tell her I was all right, but the corridors are suspiciously quiet, as if someone has banished any little miss innocent who might be contaminated by me.

As we enter her study, Miss Beale, sitting behind her desk, screws back the top of her fountain pen. It's rumoured that Miss Beale's fiancé was killed in the last war although she doesn't wear an engagement ring. The one fact which we girls assume is indisputable, is that she's a virgin. Miss Beale would have been a truly nice girl in the days when nice girls didn't.

This is my advantage. I know about sex but she doesn't. Never mind that I've made a mess of it, that I've a thickening waistband and stained character. I've gone up the one ladder in this game of life which Miss Beale would never go up, even if I'm now slipping down one of its longest snakes. It's wicked of me to think like this because she has always been a nice old stick to me but, if I don't start this way, I'll be in tears by the end.

There's a faint smell of polish in the room and someone has put flowers on a little table. Is that an attempt to make me feel at home, to divulge my secrets? If it is, it will fail.

Two chairs are set opposite her desk and we sit straight backed and looking as prim and proper as is possible when we are here to admit to my misbehaviour. I dare not look at my mother. I feel not only shame for both of us but a squirming embarrassment.

'Well, Jane,' Miss Beale begins, 'You're the last girl I'd expect to get herself into this mess. I'd put you down as one of the sensible ones.'

'Yes, Miss Beale.' I stare at my lap.

Miss Beale's voice softens. 'When is your baby due?'

It's a kind query, but my mother's voice is terse as she answers for me. 'Jane's well into her fourth month.'

'I see.'

I lift my head and allow myself a quick glance at her.

Miss Beale picks up her pen and fiddles with it. 'Tell me, Jane, how many other girls in your class are involved in...' she pauses, 'how many other girls are running the risk of ending up in this situation?' She looks triumphant, as if she has been waiting for an opportunity to root out evil among her girls.

'Is that really necessary?' My mother surprises me by her apparent reluctance to play her part in this game. 'What difference can it possibly make to Jane?'

'A headmistress should know what is going on in her school.'

I'm the one to tell her, the one expected to inform on my friends, to betray them by discussing their love lives with a grey, old spinster. The words Hitler youth unfairly spring into my head.

'Come along, Jane,' prompts Miss Beale. 'You must have talked about this between yourselves.'

In my head I dare Miss Beale to sound out those words which we are allowed to use in debating class but not in conversation. Heavy petting. Sex. Sleeping with your boyfriend.

My mother changes tack. 'Answer Miss Beale, Jane. Make an effort to be helpful.'

She must be finding it difficult, this public admission of my sin, but she doesn't have to collude. She could refuse to participate in this sixties' version of the stocks, could stick up for my privacy, for the little that is left of my self-respect. But she doesn't.

I ignore her, determined to be defiant, and stare at Miss Beale, who is now saying, 'What about Rita Miller? I don't imagine for one moment she's still a virgin.'

I almost smirk. She can say the word virgin; that pure, white word full of holiness is respectable. 'I have no idea, Miss Beale. Rita is not my best friend, we just go on the bus together.'

Miss Beale gives me a look of disbelief. 'Tell me about the girls you do talk to.'

'About sex you mean? About sleeping with their boyfriends?'

That changes the atmosphere. I can almost feel my mother's rush of blood warm the room. Miss Beale flinches. What's she going to do? Confront them? March into prayers, stand behind her little table and announce, The truth is out. Sixth form girls have sex.

'We don't talk about that. Only in debates,' I add with more cheek than I should have.

My mother stiffens. Her voice sounds strained but sure. 'I have to say Miss Beale, I don't think it helps young girls to be forced to think about sexual intercourse during school hours.'

I nearly giggle. With my womb pressing on my bladder, I almost wet my knickers. Good old Mum. Sticking up for me in the only way she can, by attacking something she doesn't understand but feels instinctively is wrong.

'I hope you're not accusing the school of encouraging the girls into immorality.' Miss Beale's voice is as ice.

Mum doesn't give up. 'It's unnecessary to suggest to impressionable girls that sex before marriage is acceptable.'

Miss Beale flushes. 'I can assure you our intention was exactly the opposite.'

'Then you have failed with Jane and I have the impression you have failed with others.'

'No one else in the school is pregnant, only your daughter.'

That's mean, spiteful. That hurts me, so it must have wounded my mother. Now I loathe Miss Beale and have a love for my mother I haven't experienced for a long time. I stand up. 'Come on, Mum. This isn't getting us anywhere. Let's go home.'

Outside the school, clouds have cast a blur across the sun. A young woman is tucking a blanket across the knees of a toddler in a pushchair. The common has the air of knowing it's about to be taken over by inclement weather.

'Let's take a taxi,' Mum suggests. 'It's quite chilly now and I don't want you getting ill.' She sighs a big deep sigh. 'There's more to all this than just having a baby, you know.'

I stay silent, amazed at this new, softer tone.

'There's the potty training and all that,' she says.

Potty training? I want to laugh. 'Let's take things one at a time.'

She hugs me, right there on the pavement, and kisses me on the cheek. 'You know I only want to do what's best,' she says.

I believe her. Right now, I'm happy. I believe my mother loves me enough to want to help me and my baby. Until I ask her when she's going back to work.

'I phoned in sick.'

'Sick?' I've never known my mother tell a lie before. I've forced her to fall lower than she ever has before.

She whirls round on me. 'Yes, sick. Because that's how I feel. Sick in my stomach, sick in my heart. Sick that you could ever do this to me.' She stops as if her words are wasted on me, her slut of a daughter. 'We'd better get home and eat something. It's not the baby's fault.'

That does it. Hearing my mother use the words the baby hits me more than all the recriminations. She had a baby, me. I am to have a baby. Her first grandchild. She should be able to love my child but because the baby I am to give her is the wrong kind of baby, she can't. The tears are on my cheeks before I can stop them. 'I'm so sorry, Mum. For hurting you.'

'We'll make the best of this, though I can't think how.'

Which encourages me to ask, 'Can't I just talk to Nick? See what he has to say, to suggest?'

Her voice is toneless, a dead sound as if she hasn't the energy to be angry with me. 'If you think I'm letting him get his hands on you again, you're wrong.' As if she has just realised what she thinks of him, of the father of her grandchild, she snarls, 'I never want to see that skunk as long as I live.'

I know she means it. As far as she's concerned Nick might as well not exist. Which I can't accept. Whether or not my mother likes it, Nick is the father of my baby. There's an us in all this and a we. We share the responsibility for our child. Our baby. But I can see, from the way Mum has turned away from me, she considers the matter closed and that my burbling on about it will get me nowhere.

We settle into an uneasy truce. The letter to the clinic sits on my dressing table.

My father leaves for the office with not so much as a goodbye, to return in the evening to kiss my mother while ignoring me. My mother stays at home, (she's a supply teacher so she can work when she wants to), every now and then hurling at me, 'This escapade of yours is costing us a fortune. And where's the little creep who caused this? In hiding, that's where.'

I buy a new notebook for my 1965 diary. At least I have something to write about.

Saturday 30 January.
Sir Winston Churchill's funeral. Mum wanted to go up and be part of it if only from the pavement but she stayed at home and watched it on television with me as if there's nothing wrong and we're the best of friends!

St Luke tells us, through the story of Mary and her cousin Elizabeth, that the quickening happens in the sixth month.

My bump's growing quietly, only discernible when I'm naked. I buy a pair of black jersey slacks with an elastic waistband. With loose tops and old cotton shirts, no one will recognise my plight. One morning I feel a wriggle in my abdomen and then a flip like a very small creature turning itself in water. At last I can experience the joy of getting to know my baby.

February brings a blur of grey and brown. Naked trees stand against a cold sky, their dark branches making patterns as intricate as a finely etched print. The sun sends pale yellow streaks to highlight the grass lime green, only to retreat as sudden rain spatters windows and pavements. St Valentine's Day comes and goes with no card or phone call from Nick. At least my mother doesn't gloat.

The morning post includes an envelope with my name on it written in familiar handwriting. Mum snatches it and rips it open.

'Are you going to open all my letters?' I ask.

Mum's expression turns fierce. 'And read any you send. I've had enough of not knowing what is going on. I trusted you and look where it got me.'

I note Mum's use of the word me and wonder exactly where I fit into this drama. I seem to be simply a catalyst for making my mother's life unendurable. 'How will you know? I'll post them and then…'

'You're not going anywhere. Not on your own. From now on, I'm taking you.'

I decide that a lost temper would do me no good and that real anger, deep despair, might be best kept for later. 'At least tell me who the letter is from.'

My mother heaves her I'll-have-to-tell-her sigh. 'From that girl Rita.'

'Heavens. Wonder what she wants?' Big mistake.

'She wants to know what it's like being pregnant.' My mother's voice rises to a screech. 'I'll tell her what it's like. It's shameful and humiliating and it's breaking my heart.' She scans the letter. 'How does this girl know? That little bastard must have been talking.'

'Can I have it please?'

'No.' My mother tears at it, across one way and another.

I'm determined to keep a grip. There's a long way to go with the three of us in this house. 'We can't keep this a secret for ever.'

'I can do my bloody best. If you think I'm letting you ruin what is left of my life, you're wrong.'

Remembering Miss Beale's possible interrogation of the sixth form, I need to warn Rita. I write a short note and, breaking my mother's rules, walk around the corner and push it through Rita's letter box.

One afternoon, the front door bell rings as though the national grid's on purple hearts. She's leaning against the door jamb, arms folded, one leg crossed over the other at her ankles, her toes pushing through the end of her blue sandals. Not wearing a coat but only a skirt and sweater.

'Rita.' The jump in my voice betrays my almost pathetic delight in seeing her, my friend from my days of assumed innocence, maybe my ally in this wasteland I inhabit.

'Your mum here?'

'Shopping.' I lead the way into the kitchen. 'Coffee?'

She thrusts a hand into a small bag which hangs from her shoulder and pulls out a packet of cigarettes.

'Better not,' I say quickly. 'Mum'll notice. Did you get my note?'

She stuffs the packet back. 'We had a proper ticking off at school.'

'She didn't tell you to keep away from me, did she?'

'We got the definite impression that your mum wasn't keen on anyone keeping up.'

The idea that a headmistress can interrogate a sixth form about their love lives, or more accurately sex lives, is an anachronism these days. With the morning-after pill available from the school nurse, the assumption is that most girls will at least make a mistake now and again. Since many couples never marry, the stigma of illegitimacy has long gone. That's certainly an improvement on the state of things in the sixties. After all, it wasn't the baby's fault.

I make instant coffee, silently trying to put on a brave face. 'Seen Les recently?' Maybe he's told Rita what exactly Nick is doing.

'He's broke.' Rita shrugs. 'They always are when it suits them.'

That's that then.

'If I've been sent an invite to the wedding, it's lost in the post.' Rita stirs sugar into her coffee as though it's going out of fashion.

I hesitate. I should stay loyal to Nick, after all what's the point of marrying him if I can't do that much?

'Nick's no good, Jane.' She drowns her advice with a huge gulp of caffeine.

An anger which I don't want surges through me. Rita might be right but it's a truth which doesn't help. I don't want advice which pushes me away from the only path I can take. I don't need encouragement to doubt Nick's intentions. 'What do you know about Nick?'

'He's a bloke no different from any other. You're better off on your own.'

'Like you? Using men for whatever you can get from them?'

'At least I haven't got a bun in the oven.'

'How can you possibly know what I want, what's good for me, when I'm having a baby and you're not?'

'I do know that once you don't have it inside you anymore, you'll feel relief.'

'I have to make a home for my baby, I love my baby…' To my horror a blur of tears masks Rita.

She puts a hand on my arm. 'Don't get all het up. It's not good for the baby. Just promise me one thing.'

I sniff and nod.

'Imagine being stuck with Nick when you're broke and tired out with a kid, with no money and no love. Seeing that it's love you seem hung up about, ask yourself if Nick loves you.' She slings her bag over her shoulder. 'Got a bloke to see.'

Which makes me laugh. 'You're just as hopeless as I am. You keep going back.'

She looks me straight in the eye. 'Not to the same one. I'll do that when I'm ready and when I've found the right one, not because I'm caught by some silly mistake.'

After she's gone I lie on my bed, arguing with myself. I'm right and Rita's wrong. Rita can't know how I feel. Missing a period and feeling sick in the morning doesn't compare with having a baby which fills your belly. A baby can't be cancelled out by swallowing a pill; a baby can't be flushed away in the school cloakroom or washed off your knickers.

However, Rita's words won't go away. Imagine being stuck with Nick when you're broke and tired out with a kid, try to imagine life with no money and no love … ask yourself if Nick loves you.

I knew Rita was talking sense. I was confused, not understanding how Nick could act so irresponsibly when there was a child in the picture. With many more years behind me, after bringing up children, I can understand that it's not a crime to run away from responsibilities, although it is a weakness. I suppose we all do it at some time or another. Now, I have plenty of sympathy with the young man that was Nick, although I still think he could have tried harder to provide for his small family to be.

My version of the truth had to win. I had no choice. To give my baby a home, I had to marry Nick.

Five

The relatively calm atmosphere in the house does not last. My mother decides I am unclean, only to be let out if she can disguise me.

The Saturday after Rita's visit is gloomy. Clouds hang heavy, but it is too warm for snow. My black slacks are too much of a weight on my legs and the elastic waistband is beginning to pinch. I'm in my room, trying to read but actually summoning up the courage to approach my mother about a maternity dress or smock or whatever it is I should be wearing, when she calls out to me.

'Jane, come down here a minute.'

Hearing her imperious tone, I shut my book. Pulling myself up by my stomach muscles is not yet impossible but doing so reminds me I have more inside me than cornflakes. A real tiny person, a fusion of me and Nick and, whatever my parents do, they can't take that away from me.

Mum and Dad are in the dining room, seated at the table. It's ten o'clock in the morning. Who do they think they are, Lord and Lady Muck, waiting to have their portrait painted?

'Put on your school raincoat,' my mother orders.

I frown. 'What for?'

'Obey your mother.' My father looks uncomfortable as if they are about to conduct torture worthy of the Spanish Inquisition.

Wearing my raincoat, leaving it hanging open, I stand in front of them.

'Button it up,' snaps my mother.

I do up all three buttons.

They appraise me as if they've never seen it on me before, my mother wearing her look-what-you're-doing-to-me-now face.

Eventually she says, 'What do you think, Gerald?'

Dad coughs. 'I think we should go if that's what you want.'

I want to be in on the secret. 'Go where?'

'Your mother wants to pop down to the coast. To see her sisters and the rest of the family.'

I cheer up. Ever since I can remember, we've spent a week in Hastings, the town where Mum lived as a girl. I love the place; the pebbly beach, the waves crashing against the stones, the cliffs offering either the ruined castle or a breezy walk. Mostly I love my aunts, the uncles and the gossiping which went with doing the rounds of their various houses. But why now, in moody February? 'Rather early for a day by the sea?'

'That's why I'd like to go.' My mother's voice is dry, unexcited. She puts a hand to her brow. 'A young girl's coat wouldn't touch her body the way yours is doing. What do you really think, Gerald?'

'I can't say I've ever noticed but you're probably right.'

I stare at my father. Why is my mother probably right? All my life my father has talked to my mother as though she was probably wrong. Then I remember. Everything's different.

'What have I done wrong now?' Clearly something's my fault. Or my raincoat's fault. 'Why have I paraded in my raincoat?'

Looking even more uncomfortable, my father says, 'Your mother wanted to see if we could take you with us without anyone noticing…' he pauses.

I see my baby inside me, pink and happy, being suffocated with the thick grey blanket of secrecy. 'You mean if I keep my raincoat on all day everyone will wonder why and if I take it off they'll be bound to notice my bump? And that's the last thing you want.' The last sentence said with a dismal finality.

My mother pushes her chair back. 'You don't think I'm going to announce it to all my family as if I'm proud of it, do you?'

'Can't I come then?' I sound like the sad little girl I am, being left behind on a family outing, being denied a treat.

'That's not the point.' She walks to the door and then turns back. 'The point is, I can't go. I can't take you down there like you are but I daren't leave you here on your own. I can't see my family until this whole business is over.' She leaves the room, weeping.

My father and I look at each other as if weighing up how to deal with this new disaster. Upstairs, the noise of my mother opening the drawer of her dressing table to find a clean hanky and then of her blowing her nose tells us she's putting a brave face on it.

'There you are,' says my father.

'Where am I? Mum doesn't rush down to the coast every other minute. Not in February. Why now all of a sudden?'

He stares out into the garden, where the clouds have turned to drizzle, imitating our despair. 'She needs the comfort of her family.'

'I don't, I suppose? What does Mum think is going to happen? That if no one knows about me, I'll disappear?'

'Forget yourself for once and consider how much you have hurt your mother.'

Still wearing my coat, I go to my room, open the door of my wardrobe and look at myself in the full-length mirror. Mum's right. The buttons of the coat sit on my middle like cherries on a cake, sticking up and out, as if straining to prove that my abdomen's full and fertile. However much I hold myself in, the bulge proves to the world I am big with child.

It isn't only my bump which gives me away. My face is pale, evidence I don't get out for long healthy sessions on the netball pitch anymore, my eyes ringed with purple and my cheeks drawn. I don't look anything like the popular image of a youngster; more like one of those characters in kitchen-sink dramas, suffering hardship and deprivation.

I wake the next morning to hear my mother's voice on the telephone. 'If you could manage that, we'll look forward to seeing you.' And the click of the receiver being replaced.

When I go down, Mum is making toast. 'Two slices, Jane?' She smiles.

Immediately I am suspicious. 'Who are we looking forward to seeing?'

'Fiona. She's coming for lunch on Sunday. Let's see what she has to say about all this.' She hugs me, quickly but still a hug.

My spirits soar. Fiona will make Mum see sense. I send a thank you to Him-up-There.

When Fiona arrives, they have a sherry and we talk, all of us avoiding the obvious. As if life is the same as always. It amazes me how grown-ups can do this, just pretend something isn't happening. But after lunch (roast beef with Yorkshire pudding, scrumptious) Mum and Dad wash up, leaving me with our guest.

'I need to talk to you,' I say baldly.

'Your mother's the one you should be talking to, Jane.'

Which I think a bit hard. She must know what Mum is like. 'They threw Nick out.'

'You can't blame them.'

'I can blame my mother for offering to gouge my insides out with knitting needles.' Talking about my mother's cruel threat makes my voice wobble.

Fiona shudders. 'That bad?' She promises to help, 'but my way, OK?'

Mum and Dad come in and I'm sent out so that, in my mother's words, 'We can discuss this business in private, Jane.' I wait for Fiona to say I should stay but she doesn't so I go to my room and write to Nick.

Later, I'm called down. 'Well?' I demand, not caring about being polite. 'It's my life and my baby you've been talking about.'

Mum goes to make tea and Dad follows her.

Fiona lights a cigarette. 'We talked. About you and the baby.'

No mention of Nick. My heart quickens. My baby's future depends on Fiona giving me the right kind of help. I keep my voice steady but it's not easy. 'Did you talk about Nick? Did they say we could get married? Then all this fuss and bother would stop. Arguing all the time won't make the baby go away although sometimes it seems Mum thinks it will.'

'You need to stop fighting your mother.' Fiona's calm, as if it really will work out. 'There is a way through all this.'

I feel light headed. 'Nick gives me a wedding ring and we live with his mother.'

'If you do that, you'll never see your mother again. Is that what you want? Don't answer that,' she adds. 'Your mother needs you as much as you need her and taking yourself off to the other side of London is not the answer.'

Which isn't what I want to hear. I feel let down, which makes me angry and rude. 'What's your brilliant solution?'

'Your mother will tell you. Eventually.'

'When the baby comes, Nick and me, we'll be a family.'

Fiona gives me a long, slow look. 'It might not hurt to remember that you are part of your mother's family and, whatever she's said to you, she does love you.'

After Fiona has left I hear Mum saying, 'I knew Fiona would have a good idea. I'll make that phone call as soon as I can admit my daughter's disgusting behaviour to a stranger.'

I'm too scared to ask about their scheming.

March comes in with the lion and my mother turns into one. I stare at her, horrified and fascinated. She'd been to the hairdresser that morning and her brown hair is transformed into a copper mane. Wearing her navy coat, she carries a new black handbag over her arm, royalty style. 'Get your coat, Jane. Brush your hair but no makeup. I don't want you looking like a tart.'

I wince. 'Where are we going?'

'I'm taking you to a moral welfare worker.'

I match her crude language. 'What the bloody hell for?'

She allows herself a smile of triumph. 'That's exactly why. You're completely out of control.' She blinks as if there's something she can't quite get to grips with. 'Fiona does some charity work with girls like you. Why she bothers, I have no idea, but it seems a moral welfare officer can help us with…' she reaches for the words, 'the intolerable situation you have put us in.'

'It's not moral welfare I need. It's Nick.'

'We'll see about that. Even if you are allowed to see him, I'll be present.'

'Why?' I make the single syllable spread into two sounds as if it can't possibly express my incredulity any other way.

'I'm not leaving you two alone together. After what you've been up to?' Her voice rises.

'What the hell…'

'Don't swear at me.'

'…do you think we're going to do? Have sex on the dining room table?' I'm amazed at my bold manner.

My mother flushes scarlet. 'There's no need to be coarse. I can't see a reason for seeing him at all.'

'Shouldn't we be married before the baby is born?'

There's a short silence during which I sense my mother wanting to hit me. She's standing close to me, looming, her right hand held taught, resting on the top of a chair. It would be the work of a moment for her to raise her hand and take a knock at my head. I want to duck but keep absolutely still. If she hits me, I want it to hurt. I want her to regret it.

But she doesn't. Instead, her cold voice telling me that the debate is over, she says, 'I'd rather be dead than see you marry that cunning little swine. We'll see what the moral welfare worker has to say about illegitimate babies.'

It's as if my mother has resigned herself to her fate so she can be the tragedy queen.

Like a bitch ready to be mated by any cur, I have to be kept on the lead. We walk along the high road, past the butcher, the baker, not-quite the candlestick maker and a Chinese restaurant. On the right-hand side of the road is a bingo hall, on the left a brand new Odeon, showing three films at once. The old theatre has been turned into a bowling alley and there's the Locarno. Not quite as hip as the Hammersmith Palais, the Locarno is the centre for all that's decadent. Ballroom dancing, rock, jive, the Twist, you can do the lot at the Locarno. I'd never been there, or the bingo hall. Both are out of bounds. My mother's quite clear on this. Nice girls don't hang around these kinds of places, but I get a kick out of walking past the dance hall and absorbing the atmosphere of the goings-on.

I turn my head away from a shop called Your Baby. I can't bear to look, can't stand the pleasure I might feel, gazing at cots and prams. Pleasure I'm not allowed to enjoy.

We continue past a huge Victorian pub. Dark red brick, pebble glass windows, green paint, all filthy. As the day is one of those bright and cheerful ones heralding spring, the doors are open. The air stinks of warm beer, cigarette smoke and slept-in clothes. I glance inside. Two old codgers sit on a bench against a wall staring out, ignoring their dusty round table with a stalk of a leg and two half-drunk glasses of pale ale. I sympathise, since I'm also one of society's misfits. Needing advice on moral welfare, I'm less than those two old men, who have simply been forgotten by the world. After this afternoon, my status as an unmarried mother, a government statistic, will be official.

Pinned to the door of 29A the High Street is a notice typed on a small, scruffy square of yellow paper. Mrs Bird Welfare 1st Floor. Come straight up.

I push open the door and put my foot on the first tread of linoleum covered stairs.

'I never dreamt,' says my mother's voice behind me, 'I'd ever be taking my daughter to a place like this.'

The staircase smells of the school cloakroom on a wet day plus a sniff or two of fouled shoes. I plod up, counting my mother's footsteps behind me. Ten, eleven, twelve… By the time I reach the top, I'm short of breath like an overweight chain smoker.

Another door. Another note. Same paper. Same typeface. 'Ring the bell and enter.'

My mother reaches across my shoulder and presses the bell. I never knew anyone could be so vicious with a button. The responding trill of 'Come in' manages to sound both inviting and repelling. The handle on the door is one of those round Bakelite ones. I walk through the space made by my mother stepping back in exaggerated politeness.

The office is small and dim, the only window overlooking an inner courtyard. There's a table with a typewriter on it and a woman sitting behind it, round face with spectacles on her nose and a smug smile under it. The face says, 'Good afternoon. We're expecting you, Mrs Courtney.' The face ignores me. 'Do sit down. Mrs Bird won't keep you waiting long.'

I want to run so turn my back on the face. I don't want to look at it because, if I do, I'll shout, See me? This is my life here this morning. I'm trapped.

My mother shoves me towards two chairs set against a blank wall. Two chairs, I register, meaning that most people bring someone with them. A friend maybe. Or maybe their mother. Or maybe not. I sit down, back straight, face composed. They can take a mug-shot for their blasted files if they want to, brand me a juvenile delinquent. My imagination isn't colourful enough because what I don't reckon to be is self-indulgent.

'I can count on one hand,' Mrs Bird is saying, ten minutes later, 'the number of my girls who just don't care.'

I'm unrepentant. We've been with this potty woman for too long already. Even though she hasn't stood up, I can tell Mrs Bird is tall by the way she bends forward over her desk towards us, her nose pointing towards my mother. Her hair's wiry, her eyes over-cooked currants like the ones which roll off the top of your bread and butter pudding and sit on the tablecloth in pairs looking back at you. Her voice is the squawking of a bird that didn't get the worm. 'All my girls regret what they've done. Most are ashamed. I rarely get one who is proud of her behaviour. Like your daughter.'

My mother shakes her head. 'I don't understand her.' Her voice breaks dramatically as if the role of the fallen woman belongs to her.

'I don't understand either.' My voice is too loud for politeness but not angry enough for downright rudeness. 'I don't understand what I've done wrong.'

They both look at me, scandalized.

I twist my hands in my lap, determined not to cry. 'I mean I know what I've done wrong, but I don't know why what I've said is wrong. All I've said is we want to get married.'

My mother draws in her breath. 'I've never heard anything so ridiculous in all my life.'

'Why,' Mrs Bird asks me, 'do you want to do that?' She speaks to me as if she's writing on a sheet of lined foolscap paper, not making conversation with another human being.

I'm silenced. I wonder if she's had a baby, even had sex recently. Was she a virgin when she married? Course she was. She's moral. Mrs Bird is an example to me and my type. For a moment we play the staring each other out game, both deciding whether to be cooperative or antagonistic. She clearly isn't going to persuade Mum to let me marry Nick, so I don't want anything to do with her. I don't need to be here. It's my mother who needs this official endorsement, this screen of respectability. I decide to state the obvious.

'We love each other, and we are going to have a baby. The way I see it, that adds up to marriage.' I sit back to wait, sensing that my mother's waiting too.

Mrs Bird turns the screws. 'You don't feel any remorse for what you have done?'

I keep silent.

The screws are tightened. 'Not for what you've done to your poor mother?'

I glance at my mother. She looks wretched, sad and tired and thinner in the face. Her eyes are still blinking but they have none of her old sparkle which made her my mum. I feel a twinge of guilt. Guilt rather than remorse because although I can accept that I have made her look so down, that the state I'm in has made her sad and worn-out, I still don't regret what Nick and I did together. The going to bed stuff. It just didn't occur to me, during those secret cuddles with Nick, that mother was involved at all. It doesn't, does it? I mean, when you are letting your boyfriend do what he has been pleading with you to do for months, the last person you think of is your mother. If only I can convince Mum and Mrs Bird how much we love each other and that this isn't some pretend game we've been playing. Can't they understand I want to do the right thing?

However, I sound as pathetic as my mother looks. 'We only did what people do when they are in love. Now, we want to do what's best for our baby.'

Mrs Bird's voice takes on an efficient note. 'That's why I am here. To help you decide what is for the best.'

My declaration of love, of good intent, has been ignored. I'm still a bad lot, not deserving forgiveness.

My new helpmeet smiles at my mother. 'I think we had better go along the line we agreed on the telephone.'

My mother nods.

Alarm bells clang in my head. 'What line?'

Mrs Bird writes in her file. 'You will come and see me each week.'

'Every week?' I don't care if I sound rude. 'What for?'

'We can have a little talk. About what will happen to your baby.'

The word baby hangs in the air, sounding defiled. When I say the word, privately in my head, it's a soft word, written in pastel shades of tenderness. Here in this squalid office, spoken by Mrs Bird, the word is harsh, carved in monochrome, with sharp edges. Baby. Pregnancy. A judgement.

I don't want to report to this woman, as if I'm under some kind of curfew. I don't want to hear my baby defiled. But I don't say so. I'm cowed by the formality of this scene, by the thick file on Mrs Bird's desk. Silence is my weapon but it's a poor one compared with righteous indignation.

'When exactly is this baby due?' Mrs Bird is asking my mother.

'Round about the middle of June.' My mother is using her telephone voice, like a porcelain tea cup, round, thin and difficult to get a handle on. 'We can't be sure. I mean…' She trails off and, to my horror, fumbles in her handbag for her hanky, twisting the small square of white linen between her fingers, rolling it into a ball to clutch in the palm of her hand as if it is a lifesaver.

'Don't upset yourself.' Mrs Bird shuffles the papers on her desk. 'This will sort itself out.'

Which makes the inside of my head fuzzy, full of a rush of thoughts. My baby is not a this and doesn't need sorting out. It's Nick I should be with, not these two snivelling and clucking women. I stand up, clutching the back of my chair for support. 'You can forget whatever you're planning. We're having the baby together. Nick and me. We're giving our baby a home.'

The silence which follows, more disturbing than my outburst, is broken by my mother blowing her nose and saying feebly, 'But we hardly know him.'

My heart beats tightly and quickly. My chest hurts. 'That's because you don't want to know him. You don't want me to grow up, to have a boyfriend, to break away from you at all. You don't want me to do anything and you never have. You've never asked Nick what he wants, not once.'

'Well Jane,' says Mrs Bird. 'Perhaps you'd better give me the young man's address and telephone number and I'll ask him to come and talk to me. How would that do?'

I sit down.

We walk back in silence. I notice a wool shop and promise myself to buy a couple of ounces and a pattern after my next visit to Mrs Bird. If I don't start knitting baby clothes soon the poor little mite will be naked.

Back at home, I write to Nick to warn him about hearing from Mrs Bird.

Today social workers have quite a different meaning to the public. They are connected to truancy, bad parenting and, in the worst scenario, crimes such as child prostitution. Now, thinking of my social worker, I pity her. Even her name gave her a disadvantage. Mrs Bird: too easy to mock.

'Mrs Cheepy-cheep,' Nick used to call her.

Mrs Bird was more like a well-meaning member of the Women's Institute or the Parish Council than a professional person. I have learned that she was employed by The Church of England Moral Welfare Board. We hadn't reached the days when council taxes (then called the rates) were spent on getting youngsters out of their wrong doings. It was left to charity. Another blow to my mother's pride. I felt sorry for Mrs Bird. How could she have any idea of the mess made out of Mum and me fighting each other and my mother fighting for her own moral code?

When, years later, I returned to the part of London where all this took place, I found the social worker's office. It was, and still is, at the far end of the High Street, a quaint name for the long main road, the A something to Brighton. It's one of those roads which exists at the edges of all large cities; wide enough in parts to be divided by brick-bound earth plots trying to give life to straggling roses, but narrowing down to a single carriageway every now and then, forcing cars to nose in front of lorries and between buses as thwarted drivers bid for space.

The road, of course, is still there, with the converted terrace house used for some kind of office accommodation. Not surprisingly. Nowadays, social workers are employed, not by charities, but by local authorities. For once in her life, in taking me to Mrs Bird, my mother was ahead of her times.

Six

Finally, a letter from Nick! My mother opens and reads it before giving it to me with the words, 'It seems his job at the paper wasn't all that reliable after all.'

What on earth is she on about? My hands are shaking as I read the words.

Jane, my sweet,

Forgive the delay. I've changed my job. I hope this is what you want. I start work next Monday in a print workshop. Pa arranged the interview but I charmed the old geezer running the place and he offered me the job on the spot. I don't want to spend the rest of my life on an industrial estate off the north circular but learning about print will help me move on to the film industry.

Ma sends her love. She is knitting baby clothes and says you are welcome to live here with us. So you can stop worrying about rent for a flat or even money for food as Pa will sub us.

Love Nick

PS Don't worry about Mrs Dicky Bird. I'll charm her onto our side.

I experience a great sense of relief. He's happy to see Mrs Bird, he has a job and a plan and even though living with his mother is not the best of ideas, it's a start.

Thrusting her hand out in a quick, sharp movement, Mum snatches the letter away from me and reads it. 'What's all this about films?'

'Give it back. It's my letter.'

'You've lost the right to say anything is yours. Since you have no shame.' She stops as if she's just thought of something. 'You haven't told us, have you, when it all happened? Over at his parents' house I suppose. Another occasion when we trusted you.' She takes a step towards me. The whites of her eyes are pink; her breath on my cheek is hot. 'Did you offer yourself to him like a common whore?'

My anger cools into despair. From being a respectable and conscientious person, my mother has become a crude, hard woman. Have I done that? I open my mouth, 'I'm sorry, Mum. I didn't mean…'

'What did you mean then? Or didn't you think at all, you just let him do as he wanted with you, was that it? You make me sick.' The words come in a spurt of spittle which hits my cheeks like stale rain.

A new kind of fear whirls inside me. I'm scared. Does my mother really see me as a loathed and despised creature? My mother sees me, not as her daughter, but as a girl outside her own world, an outcast, a leper. If so, if that's how it is, I have nothing to lose. I might as well fight back. 'It wasn't like that. You've got it all wrong.' In anguish I try, 'Weren't you ever in love?'

'Don't talk to me about love. This isn't love. Lust more like, although I wouldn't expect a young girl to understand that. Has he been ringing you?'

I shake my head. 'You can't stop me writing to him though, can't stop me seeing him. Maybe if I went over there...'

My mother takes a deep breath. 'From this day you do not go outside this house.' She pauses. 'Apart from seeing Mrs Bird.'

Panic. This is worse than I've imagined. 'You can't,' I shout at her. 'You can't make me a prisoner.'

'I can do whatever I like. As your mother, I'm responsible for you. It will be best if you remember that from now on.'

I stumble on the next words as, already, I'm beginning to wonder if I still believe myself. 'We want this baby.'

'He hasn't exactly been rushing round here to find out how you are, has he?'

'You threw him out.' I want to hurt her as she's hurting me, but right at that moment something twitches inside me, something moves deep in the middle of my bump. My baby. My baby is calling me to calm down, to be positive if I could not be loving.

I try being patient. 'If Nick has a new job with more money I should see him, make plans.' Then I add, not to goad her but because it seems common sense, 'the baby is not going to go away.'

A mistake. Her face colours. 'I know that. I know you let that dirty little snitch ruin you, making us all a laughing stock.'

'But no one else knows.'

Her breathing becomes faster, as if she can't get quite enough oxygen for all the anger she needs. 'I know. Your father knows. Your doctor knows. Your school friends know. Isn't that enough?' She reaches out for my arm as if to catch hold of me, but I quickly skirt her and run out of the kitchen. She follows me up the stairs and into my bedroom where I am cornered. She holds me by both arms above the elbow and shakes. And shakes.

My head rocks backwards and forwards, I bite my lip and all the time I am shouting, 'What are you doing?'

'Trying to make you see sense and to get into your head that you are not seeing Nick or anyone else. You're seeing no one who might give you the slightest encouragement. I've had enough.'

'Stop!' I am crying now. 'You'll hurt the baby.'

She pushes me backwards and I land on my bed. My arms are hot and sore. I am trembling but with relief. I don't look at her but curl up my body and shut my eyes.

'You can bloody well stay there until your father comes home. We'll see what he has to say about all this seeing people.'

She slams the door behind her.

It was as if my mother had given up the fight. She returned to teaching, leaving me with the threat of, 'If you dare to see that boy without my permission, I will throw you on his mercy.'

If there was one person who opted out of all the rumpus about me it was my father, who'd uttered hardly a word to me since that day we told them. I'd lost my mother already, but whether forever or just for the next few months, I had no idea. I was on my own

One wet afternoon, I find and read Nick's letters, all painstakingly written in copper plate, to find promises of everlasting love. But his words are always centred on himself: I will love you until the moon goes out or the sun stops shining, I have been trying to analyse love and can't thank you for loving me, I need someone to lean on, you must tell me everything, no secrets or our love means nothing, and finally, If I am going to be a father it is as God wishes. Never mind God, what about what I wish or need?

While the only things on my mind are what would happen to me and my baby, the phrases he wrote were all about his world, his circumstances: new job, live with mother and Pa will sub us. The new job is an achievement but neither the idea that his pa would keep us or that we would live with his ma fills me with joy or trust. I should have made my escape months before, when he took me over to East London, to see his doctor. But, then, I fancied we were in love.

I'm enjoying the one blissful advantage of my pregnancy, sitting in the kitchen listening to a radio play, when the front door bell rings. Which is a bother. I don't want to be disturbed. I clear my throat and call, 'Who is it?'

'It's me, Jane. Nick.'

He's come to see me. He does care.

I open the door, pulling it right back. 'Quickly. I don't want anyone to see you.'

'Bit cloak and dagger.' Nick pushes past me, straight into the lounge. 'Are you alone?'

83

'Mum's at work.'

We haven't been in this room since the day we told my parents about the baby, back in December. It's now March. We stand with a cool distance between us. I wait for his kiss, but he doesn't move. Eventually I offer coffee.

'Great. Any toast? I haven't eaten yet.'

'Since when?' I don't care if I sound inhospitable. Why hasn't he kissed me? Why hasn't he put his arms round me and hugged me and his baby?

In the kitchen, he eats his toast rapidly and gulps coffee. 'I can't stay long. Just had the chance to pop in. How are you?'

A numb coldness sweeps through me. I see him as I've never seen him before. 'How am I? How the bloody hell do you think I am?'

He gives me a sideways glance.

I realize he's not looked me straight in the eye, not once. I can't help raising my voice. 'You walk out… '

'I was thrown out.'

'You went easily enough…' I stop. I have to try harder. I have no choice. I have no one else. He's supposed to love me. I ignore the devil's voice in my head saying, *Your mother's supposed to love you.* 'Nick, what we are going to do?'

Then he looks at me, as if he's changed his mind about me since he's arrived. 'The job's going well, Janey. Not much money but it's a start.'

I'm swinging on a rainbow! 'That's great. Doing what?'

He grins at me. 'D'you know, some of the time I'm not entirely sure.'

The rainbow ends in a cloud.

'Only kidding. It's nothing grand, clerk in a print factory but at least it's arty.'

Which irritates me. Nick's pipe-dream of being arty doesn't tie in with being a responsible husband and father. 'How does that help?'

He rubs the side of his nose and winks. 'Might be a way in.'

'Way in to what?'

'Films, Hollywood, the big time. I reckon to be a set designer. Come on Jane, be pleased for me.'

I had to get this conversation back to a sensible level. 'How much are you earning? Can we afford a flat? When can we…?'

'Hold on, not so fast.'

'Not so fast? Nick, biology might not be your strong point but this baby's going to arrive when it's ready. It won't wait, not even for you.'

'Are you telling me that we'll be allowed to get married? I had the distinct impression from your mother that you and me were not meant for each other.'

'She's different now.' I'm at my most optimistic. 'Thanks for your letter. Did Mrs Bird ring you?'

'She did.' He pulls a face. 'I don't need some busybody heckling me. It's bad enough going to the factory. You can't think, the noise, it's just not where I should be. I've got my father refusing to sub me and Ma nagging me.'

I take a deep breath. 'Nick, I've got a baby inside me. One I didn't want but now I do. You and I are going to agree on one thing.'

He doesn't ask me what, so I add 'As long as there's a chance of being together we are going to take it. For the sake of the baby. Do you understand?' He doesn't reply and I'm afraid he's going to walk out on me again. I choke on my words. 'We've no choice, Nick. The clock won't turn back.'

He stands up, pulling me towards him. 'It's all right. Don't cry. I love you and the baby. I'll make it all right. You'll see.' He kisses me, a long kiss. I respond, desperate for anything between us which proves we're still together.

He lets me go. 'When will your mother be back?'

'She usually gets home about half-past four.'

'Fancy half an hour in bed? I haven't had…'

Disgusted, I push him away. 'Neither have I. And d'you know what? I don't want it. Not anymore. But a little kindness would be welcome. A hug, a cuddle.'

'Come on Janey,' he wheedles. 'I'll cuddle you in bed.'

I lie. 'It's not safe for the baby. Not for another month. Are you going to tell me about Mrs Bird or not?'

He puts his right hand in the air, flapping his fingers against his thumb in the 'birdy' gesture. 'Tweet, tweet. You know I'll do anything if it means we can be together. I told her we could live with Ma.'

'Ma?' I was almost in tears again. 'Why not on our own?'

'No money, Janey. Landlords ask for key money ….'

Key money? I have no idea what he is talking about. I was defeated. 'So I'll ask Mum if you can come to lunch to talk about getting married?'

Nick kicks the leg of the table and looks anywhere but at me. 'Suppose so.' Then he hugs me, telling me I'm his very own Janey and I'm weakening and almost letting him take me to bed when he says, 'Got to rush. Just tell your mother I'm earning and I'll be in touch. Love you.'

I almost slam the door behind him. Why did he bother to come? I ask myself. Apart from the obvious and I'm sure he wasn't serious. Was it really just to see me? This sounds too good to be true, but I convince myself I am right. I tell myself that with him earning regularly and caring about me and the baby, things look brighter. I must play my part, trot along to see Mrs B and keep hoping.

I enjoy my next session with Mrs B although it has an element of farce about it.

'I saw Nick,' she tells me. 'Isn't he charming? I can see why you fell for him.'

Isn't the woman supposed to be supporting the good and the virtuous?

When I say nothing she says, 'He has a job. Quite a good one, I understand.'

A good one? I try to imagine exactly what he's told her but fail. However, I keep to my newly optimistic mood and we finish by agreeing to see what happens and to be patient.

Whatever Nick said, did or did not do, I'm having a baby and a baby has to be clothed. On the way home from Mrs B, I take some money out of my post office book to buy some wool.

I haven't knitted since I left school but, if I'm going to have a baby, I'm going to have to knit. In the shop in the High Street, I choose a pattern for a matinee jacket with a matching bonnet and mittens and some blue wool, reckoning that a girl can wear blue but a boy can't be seen in pink. I have enough money to buy that and the two pairs of needles I need.

The woman behind the counter smiles. 'That'll knit up lovely. Is it for a friend's baby?'

'No mine.' After my session with Mrs Bird, that feels good. But only for two seconds.

The woman raises her eyebrows at me. 'Really? You don't look old enough.' Then she stares in a pointed way at my ring finger. Which doesn't have a wedding ring. Not even an engagement one. She frowns and her mouth turns down. She's judging and condemning.

I blush and snatch the paper bag from her, wanting to get out of that shop by yesterday. But it's too late. I've seen how it will be, what people will think once I'm not able to hide what I am. An unmarried mother. Not exactly a slut, as my mother called me, but I might as well be for the disapproving looks I'll get.

Back in the relative safety of my home, I'm calmer. I turn on the electric fire in the lounge, make myself a cup of tea and settle down, kidding myself I'm a regular mother-to-be. For the first time since that terrible day we told my parents, in spite of nosey Mrs Bird, I'm cosy, comfortable and almost happy.

All the while my baby's growing. That evening, on impulse, I take off all my clothes and study the reflection of my naked body. Dark nipples on full breasts. A firm swelling between my hips, my skin taught, my belly-button dimpling the dome. I put a hand on my bump and touch hardness, a large egg building itself a stronger shell while it perfects its creamy yolk. Challenging me with its existence. It forces the question, what will I do when I can't hide this any longer. When I can't remain at home?

In spite of my doubts, of all the trouble it's causing, I'm glad of the physical proof of my baby. My lumpy body gives me a presence I haven't had before, and I like it.

I'm not afraid of the future, although I should be.

I knit another four matinee jackets but still have no other baby clothes. My store of pocket money has run out and my parents aren't offering.

Nick telephones once to report on his meetings with Mrs Bird. He sounds cheerfully optimistic enough. 'Don't worry, Jane, I'm getting on with Dicky-Bird. She really is a sweet old thing.'

Which doesn't say to me, I've arranged things with the registry office and we'll be married soon.

Sometimes I find it difficult to believe this is happening to me and on other days I silently scream at the frustration of it all. Meals are still taken more or less in silence, my father reading the newspaper and my mother sitting with her pained expression, chewing slowly and deliberately as if eating is her final pleasure in life.

When we aren't quarrelling.

'I saw Mrs Bird today,' I begin brightly one evening at supper. 'She says it's time I clocked in at the hospital. She says I should be seeing a doctor.'

'You're healthy enough,' says my mother. 'In my day there wasn't all this fuss about clinics.'

'If I don't, there might not be a hospital bed for me when the time comes.'

'You'll be over with Nick's mother, won't you? Isn't that the plan? Aren't you waiting for him to come and rescue you, take you away from us?'

Anger rises inside me. Anger at the proof my mother couldn't care less about what happens to me, let alone my baby. 'Isn't that what you want? For me to go away? To take my disgrace away so that it won't trouble you?'

'There wouldn't have been any trouble if we'd never let that little piece of shit inside this house.'

I can hardly believe my ears. Have I done this, brought my proud mother down to the level of a fishwife? If I have, if I'm solely responsible for making her resort to the language of the foulest dockside, then I am ashamed.

Mum's face is red, her lips rolling together while she thinks of what to say next. 'When I think of all the trouble he's caused, of all the hurt I've been made to feel just because that little runt stuck his dick inside you to get a bit of satisfaction…'

My father looks across to her with pain in his eyes. 'That's enough of that. Don't upset yourself. Jane, you'd better go to your room and give your mother some peace.'

I didn't usually confide in my father but suddenly I change my mind. Maybe he'll listen to me. 'Why can't I marry Nick, Dad?'

But his face turns sour and he scowls. 'If you think I'm letting you tie yourself up with a person so low… it's out of the question.'

Which puts me completely out of patience with either of them. 'Well,' I snap back, 'Something has to happen or this baby's going to be born on the kitchen floor. And then what will the neighbours think?'

Seven

My mother does try, when it suits her. My diary records,

Mum is making a maternity dress. Without me asking her to. I'm staggered. It's quite pretty, blue with a yoke and then the gathered bit to cover the bump. It has a white Peter Pan collar, very Virgin Mary.

They call me down as soon as my father arrives home from the office. To my surprise, they look pleased and almost happy for the first time since they knew about the baby. For just a second, I think they're going to say everything will be all right, that they will arrange the wedding, help us find a flat and will love their grandchild. My mother is right. I am a fool.

'Sit down Jane,' she says. 'We have something to tell you.'

My father clears his throat, which should make me suspicious. Since when has he had anything to do with all this? Mum had taken over, or so it seemed until this evening. She's saying, 'Fiona rang me at work today. She's spoken to Mrs Bird and it's all settled.'

Any hope of a wedding or a happy ending vanishes. A cold stone settles in my chest as my baby does a quick flip and settles itself down to listen.

'We had no idea,' says my mother, her eyes bright, 'that such places existed.'

'What places?'

'For girls like you who have brought disgrace on their families.'

I understand that whatever is to happen to me has allowed my mother to see me in a new light. I might have behaved atrociously, I might have let her down, but in some way, I have become interesting. Almost respectable. My mother can now fit me into a scheme, a way of dealing with me and my problem which will take care of her own embarrassment and shame.

My father does some more throat clearing. 'We don't want you to misunderstand, Jane. It isn't as if we don't want you here, although,' and he looks at my mother, 'clearly we can't entertain any idea you bring the child back here…'

A tear escapes and rolls down my cheek. I can't help myself. I'm so cold and alone. They're talking about me and my baby as if we're subhuman, as if I don't have any feeling and as if my baby's some kind of rubbish to be disposed of when the appropriate date is reached.

'There's no need for tears, Jane.' Mum is using her clipped I've-got-the-answer voice. 'We can give you exactly what you want. To go away from here. That is what you want isn't it?'

'I want to give my baby a home and if I have to marry Nick I will.'

'Nick doesn't seem to want the same thing, does he?'

'All I need to know is what's going to happen to me now?'

'It's the obvious thing,' my mother says. 'I can't think why I didn't think of it myself, but of course I didn't know anything about dealing with pregnant girls. Until now.'

I envisage a Hogarth print entitled The Punishment. Lolling in the gutter in front of a great grey workhouse are thin, worn-out women wearing smocks and drinking gin. Spilling onto the road are clutches of emaciated children with huge holes for eyes and naked feet. 'How are they dealt with then?'

'Fiona and Mrs Bird have arranged it all. You are to spend the last few weeks of your pregnancy and a few weeks after your confinement, in a mother and baby home. Church of England, of course.'

Later, I hear them talking.

'The law is all wrong. In any sensible world we'd be able to sign the adoption papers.'

Adoption? Where did that spring from? I have no intention of giving away my baby. I go to sleep crying into my pillow.

How did we get to that, my mother and I? How did we reach a situation where she planned to lock me up in an institution until after the birth of my baby, intending to force me to give away her first grandchild? How did a once-loving mother and daughter become so detached that they couldn't bear to be in each other's company? Because, although I remonstrated with my mother over her scheme, although I cried and kicked against her like a spoilt teenager, although I hated her for separating me from Nick, for surely that was her aim, the idea of living away from home appealed to me.

Perverse as it might seem, I was fascinated by this place, this building which contained other girls like me. At the very least going to the home would bring freedom from my mother's tyranny.

Where was it? I wanted to know. Who was in charge? How many girls lived there? How long did they stay there?

My mother didn't know the answers. I gathered it was a place of secrecy, a place where girls were sent when their condition could no longer be hidden from the neighbours or be tolerated by their families, when the shame became public.

I persisted. 'You must know if the home is in London?'

'Of course it's in London,' she snapped.

'Where is it then?' I almost screamed at her.

She named a leafy and eminently respectable part of West London, a district I had never been to and did not know, which only increased my curiosity. 'When do I go?'

'We expect it to be soon.'

My next diary entry reads,

I know now what Mum and Fiona have planned for me. I'm to be sent away. Not exactly how I wanted it to be but ...

I still remember the questions which were so important then, questions which resolved themselves once I arrived. Were we inmates allowed out? Would I be allowed to go shopping, to take walks, to meet friends? Could I, for instance, invite Rita for tea? I can still giggle at the thought of Rita sipping tea with a group of fallen women. Most important, would I be able to see Nick? I remember my imagination racing, seeing a picture of the two of us walking on the common near to the home holding hands and making plans for our baby.

My diary entry records I posted a letter to Nick to tell him of Mum's plans but not whether he replied.

After the initial euphoria following Fiona's phone call, hell returns. Mealtimes are torture with me on the rack and an invisible gag round my mouth, so I can only scream in silence. Neither of them talks, so I read the paper. Remarks from me like, They're running a trial of moving the August Bank holiday. Can't see what the difference will be, or, No picture of mods and rockers fighting at Clacton this year are met with either a grunt or a damning comment on youngsters today. When they do talk, they talk across me. Girls like me are nothing but scum, or should be horse-whipped until they see sense and, as always, the country is going to the dogs.

There's no mention, let alone discussion, that I'm to be locked up for an indefinite time.

The day of my final visit to Mrs B, my mother comes with me. Mrs B says something about how pleased she is with me for taking this sensible decision and I sign a form applying for a place in the home. My diary entry for that day reads, No more Mrs B!!!!!!!!!!

The decision, however extreme, seems to settle my mother. Each weekday afternoon at five o'clock, she returns from wherever she's teaching, and happily offers to make me a cup of tea. We sit, her with the early evening paper and me with my knitting, in apparent harmony. With my baby flipping inside me like a healthy goldfish in its bowl, I begin to feel as if I have a life, even if an uncertain one.

The last full week of March and the morning is torn from pictures in a children's book. In the sky white wisp trails against the smooth blue, chiffon over silk. The sun, frisky as a new born lamb, is beaming on front-garden daffodils, highlighting their petals as if polished.

A letter arrives with my name neatly typed. Mum hands it over.

At the top of the writing paper is the title Streatham & District Moral Welfare Association. It is signed by Marion Bird. She writes that a Mrs Clements will expect me in the early afternoon Wednesday March 31st. Mrs B hopes I will settle down and be happy and she will visit me on the following Friday.

Mum is all brightness at supper, chatting about Fiona's efficiency and the clothes I will take with me to the home. Later, when she is in her room, I hear crying.

I feel like crying too. I wish Mum and I could talk about all this without rowing. In the darkness of my room, my imagination plays tricks of dreams coming true.

This home, whatever it is like, is my only hope for a future of any kind.

For I know, in the deepest corner of my heart, the last thing I want for my baby or for me is to live with Nick's batty old Ma or his bohemian Pa.

Eight

'I'm getting fed up with traipsing across London in this heat,' Nick said. 'How about you come over to my place for the weekend? I want to have you, Janey, so you're all mine.'

It was the start of the summer holidays, 1964. We'd been to the pictures and I was standing outside our house with him, needing to kiss him goodbye but not really wanting to do this in the street. His invitation made me suddenly happy, although I was still dubious about giving him what he wanted. I told myself that spending the weekend at his house would help me make up my mind. I needed to see Nick with his family. To understand him that much more.

Mum had laid for supper in the dining room. With its smooth, teak table, matching chairs and long, bare sideboard, the room was full of sharpness, not a place for asking permission to visit East London.

Mum was chattering in her light and happy voice, as if she'd just discovered the luxury of a room meant just for eating. 'This is the coolest room in the house.'

A bowl of lettuce and chopped cucumber sat in the middle of the table, green, healthy and boring.

'Fetch the corned beef, Jane,' I was told. 'And call your father.'

While we munched, I formed a few sentences in my head and then tried, 'Nick was over this afternoon. We went to the cinema.'

Mum looked up. 'Why didn't he come in?'

'He had to get back to the paper.' I waited a moment, sending up a small prayer. 'He's quite busy at the paper. Too busy to get over here again soon. He's asked me to spend next weekend at his parents' home.' I held my breath.

My mother said, 'I don't think we have his address, do we?'

I breathed relief over my new potatoes and ate my supper like a good girl.

Later, I wrote down his address and telephone number, my mother found Nick's road in the A-Z and reported to my father that Nick lived in a good area.

I wasn't concerned whether he lived in a grand house or not, although I was excited by the idea of spending the weekend in one. I wanted to be welcomed by his parents, to wander from room to room, seeing the side of Nick I had no idea about.

Mum gave me permission in her own way. 'I'd have preferred to meet Nick's parents first. Don't forget, we are trusting you to behave properly. Do I make myself clear?'

I rang Nick before she changed her mind. 'I can come. You'd better collect me.'

'It'll be after six on Saturday,' he said. 'Have to be at the paper all day.'

A stab of disappointment and already the weekend was spoiled. I told myself it was better than nothing and went to my room to consider which clothes to wear.

The following Saturday evening was warm with the sky a sultry, smooth grey. The air smelt of London summer, sweet over-ripe apples, with the singed lamb from back garden barbeques fighting the stink of stale rubbish. As Nick and I came out of Wanstead tube station, it began to rain, that thick, misty rain full of London dust.

'There's a bit of a walk,' Nick said.

A bit of a walk turned out to be fifteen soaking minutes crossing a forsaken grassy area, inhabited with lean trees and stringy bushes. By the time I'd trotted beside him down a pavement trimmed with dripping leaves, I was soaked to my skin through my thin dress and shivering.

Nick finally waved at a house announcing, 'The ancestral home.'

We stopped at the gate of a front garden, with unpruned rose bushes and a whiff of cat spray. I stared at the narrow middle-of-terrace house, with its tacked-on porch across the front door, chipped paint, tarnished letter box and worn coconut mat. Already I was making judgements. 'Is this where you live?'

He shrugged. 'It's not the palace your mother might have imagined but she's not here.'

I stood under the porch, gazing at the unlined curtains and hearing the sound of a television. I felt wronged, as though I had been trapped into agreeing to the plan. Immediately I was conscious of reacting like my mother would, of adding up the value of the wrong things, of making hasty decisions about people.

Nick pressed his finger on the bell button.

'Don't you have a key?' I asked.

He smirked. 'A couple of weeks ago, when Pa hadn't come home by six in the morning, Ma bolted him out. He stayed out. Ma changed the locks.'

I willed him to say he was joking. 'Your father is not here? What am I going to tell my mother?'

'Do you want to stay the night or not?'

I feared making Nick cross, so I stayed quiet.

The front door was pulled back and there stood a woman, wearing a viridian felt hat, with a tall crown and thin brim, straight out of the cast of Alice in Wonderland. Her hair, tinted red and as dry as old blooms, hung round her cheeks in ringlets. A pantomime dame, except that her face was an old lady's, soft around the mouth and eyes, the skin puckering as if someone had stapled it to make it fit her shrunken bones. She was wrapped in a cable-knit cardigan over a V-neck sloppy joe, over a chin-swaddling jersey.

As he pushed me inside the hall, Nick joked, 'You're not at the North Pole, Ma.'

This was his mother? Hardly the reliable chaperone I expected.

Ma was staring at my skirt, dripping a puddle onto the linoleum. 'I'd offer you a bath but the water's not on. Can I do you a bit of bacon and a cup of tea?'

'I'd better take these clothes off. All right if I wear my pyjamas?' I was pretending like mad, my voice full of girlish pleasure.

'You're in the spare room.' Ma made her words sound cheap.

The room was narrow with a single bed covered in a pink candlewick spread, a plain wooden chest of drawers and a single-door wardrobe, painted pink to sort of match the bedspread. I wondered if Nick's mother wanted a baby girl all those years ago. The thought was almost an omen of things going wrong.

'Chilly?' Nick pulled me to him. 'I'll pop in later and warm you up.' His kiss was long and thorough. 'Once Ma is safely tucked up in her bed.'

The church clock was striking midnight when Nick crept into my bed. I opened my eyes to give him a lazy smile. 'I left the curtains open so we could see each other.' This was romance, real love, drowning out the suggestion that I should turn him away. 'I shouldn't be letting you do this. I promised my mother.'

'Close your eyes.' He leaned into me, pressing his body along mine.

The scent of Nick's body was good: clean but slightly furry, like a picture book animal. I wanted him this close, wanted it to be just the two of us, alone and very private. We made love quickly and silently. Nick said his mother was a light sleeper. This was how I'd longed for it to be, just the two of us between the sheets. But when he whispers 'This is our secret' I think, *a guilty secret*. Nick cuddled me while I drifted in and out of sleep. Later, we had another go.

When I woke in the morning, I was alone. I understood Nick couldn't be in my bed once his mother was up, but I longed to share with him the snugness of being together when the sheets were still warm and the pillow speckled with two of his hairs. I lay listening to the birds calling, wondering whether he wanted to be close to me, to giggle about the night's achievement, about my changed status. I yearned for closeness more than naked bodies, fondness if I couldn't have love. I thought of what we'd done together and longed to hear him tell me he loved me to assuage my guilt. Because if I were not guilty of anything else, I had broken my mother's perfect-daughter code.

The front of the house faced east, the morning light making everything in my room look cheerful, even the tatty old bedspread. Nick stole along the passage to my bed and told me his mother had gone to her sister's. This time we didn't care about the bed creaking, which should have encouraged me to be enthusiastic, to prove I loved him. But I remained quietly still, watching Nick's face and wondering.

Afterwards, he kissed me on my nose. 'Get dressed. We're meeting Pa.'

My navy sling-backs clattered on the pavement, which was just about as sophisticated as I got, but I knew Nick was proud of me. He caught hold of my fingers and we swung hands.

Nick was talking about his father. 'Don't be surprised by what you find.'

'How?'

'When Ma threw him out his mistress took him in…'

'His what?'

'The woman in his life.'

'What about your mother?' I sounded scandalised. Which I was.

'Ma hasn't had Pa in her bed for years.'

102

I stood still to face him. 'Is that all there is to love then, sex?'

'Don't go all holy on me, Janey.' He shrugged. 'I thought you'd understand.'

Which made me feel mean.

Eventually, Nick stopped outside the gate of a driveway to a large house with pillars both sides of the front door and held out his arm like a showman. 'Just what madam desires.'

Perhaps I wasn't going to have to embellish for my mother after all.

But instead of walking up to the front door, Nick steered me down a side drive to the garden, telling me, 'Pa's an eccentric. You'll love him.'

At the far end of the garden, squatting under a huge chestnut tree, was a blue caravan. I saw a round, fat vehicle with a small window in the side and a shallow set of steps running up to a door. One of the wheels was broken and the caravan tilted as if to say, 'I'm not going anywhere.'

Nick grinned. 'Pa's bolt-hole. Great, isn't it?'

My bright hopes flew away. 'Given the choice of living in a tacky caravan or over there,' I nodded towards the house, 'I know where I'd choose.' I was behaving badly but already didn't care.

The path around the lawn was still wet from the previous night and my heels sunk into the gravel, sharp and cold against my heels. Leaves, shaken down by the storm, lay on the ground, brown and red, damp and soft like used blotting paper. A few dahlias were in flower, purple and yellow heads bowed by rain, the thin petals sprinkling the earth. I stopped to brush torn dandelion stalks from my ankles. 'This is a dump. Your Pa must be a fool.'

I was rejecting Pa before I'd met him, just like I had judged Ma, but I was running out of patience. As we walked closer to the caravan, the warm scents of tobacco mingled with the damp, raw atmosphere of the unkempt garden, while the lyrics of Love Me Do drowned out the cheeps of a blackbird.

Nick grabbed me by the hand. 'That could be our song.'

I scowled. 'You know what they say. Love won't pay the bills.'

We climbed the two steps and walked in without knocking.

Pa was sitting up at the draining board of his tiny sink, a board tacked with a sheet of white cartridge paper propped in front of him, drawing thick, black lines with a soft-nibbed pen. His head, with black and grey streaked hair, dipped, his back curved over his drawing board. I guess it wouldn't straighten fully when he stood up. He was wearing fawn cotton slacks and a beige shirt with charcoal stained cuffs.

'Hi Pa,' Nick said. 'I asked Janey over.'

Not turning around, he stretched out to switch off the transistor radio. 'Sit down.'

A bench along the side of the caravan was cluttered with old newspapers, spoiled sheets of paper, broken pencils and old biros. Nick swept them to the end. 'He won't be long, will you Pa? Coffee anyone?' A milk bottle stood by the side of the sink, the milk already separated into curd lumps and a pale, thin liquid.

I replied, too curtly, 'Black.'

After Nick had fixed my coffee, he pulled out his packet of Camels, lit one for himself and one for Pa. He leant over the drawing, an arm round his father's back and laughed. 'It's great Pa. Janey, have a look at this.'

I pushed myself between him and Pa. The drawing was of two men with beards, hippy types, sitting at the top of a mountain, one saying to the other, I thought we'd have a summit meeting.

Pa glanced round at me. 'This is the girlfriend?' As if I wasn't there he added, 'Pretty.'

Which was more than could be said of him. Pa had narrow eyes, a beaky nose and a thin moustache which looked as if it could do with a shot of fertilizer. There wasn't an ounce of likeness between him and his son, a fact which gave me uncharitable thoughts about poor old Ma, wondering if she'd enjoyed a moment of unfaithful passion.

Pa put down his pen and turned round. 'It's the pub then? Suppose I'm paying?' He took a wad of notes from a jam jar.

Outside, he pushed a rusty bolt across the top of the door. We crossed the garden, turned into the road and walked the fifty yards to the high street.

The Duke of Wellington was dark, crowded and noisy. We went into the public bar, Pa asking me, 'You don't mind, do you?' and of course I didn't but the men, the women even, they stank of jumble sale coats and worn socks, thick stockings in need of a wash, and a warm, between the legs mustiness, the kind of smell which made you go off sex forever.

'Cider, Janey?'

I waited while Nick and Pa drunk their first round, drawing myself inwards away from the stale beer and the fag ends. But I couldn't escape the shouting.

'So I said to 'im, I said, whatcha think you're looking at?'

'What?'

'Me, that's what. So I said to him you mind your own bleeding business.'

'And did he? Mind it?'

'Did he half. Cos if he hadn't I'd have been up the police, wouldn't I?'

'They wouldn't have helped. Not the cops. They're no bleeding use, all they want is to keep their noses clean.'

Above the racket, I could hear Nick saying to Pa, 'What d'you think Pa? Of my Janey?'

'She's sweet and pretty. Is she still as innocent as she looks?'

'You asking me to brag, Pa?'

I felt a warm sense of a secret between Nick and me. He didn't want to admit to his father that last night was our first together.

They joined me at the table. Pa handed me a glass of sweet cider. I ignored the smelly people and inhaled the rich scent of the Camels. We drank and exchanged simple pieces of news; Pa selling his cartoons to a different paper from usual, Nick managing to write his column in half a day and spending the rest reading in a City churchyard.

After a bit, Pa looked at me and said, 'Tell me about you, Jane. What plans for your future?'

I thought, I'll surprise you. 'Might go to university. To read history of art.'

He visually flinched. 'Nick didn't tell me you were clever.'

Which annoyed me. 'Didn't you, Nick?'

Nick coloured. 'I didn't think you were that bothered'

Which turned me contrary. I might have loved Nick, but he didn't own me. I shrugged. 'Not sure. I'll see.'

'You know where love leads to, don't you?' Pa winked at me. 'Wedding bells and the patter of tiny feet.'

I blushed. Nick didn't though, he just scowled sourly. A doubt slivered through me but then Pa added, 'I've always dreamed of grandchildren.'

'Really?' A light shone in Nick's eyes. He pulled me to him. 'One day. But not just yet.'

A simple happiness filled me. I had a fella. I was with him, all the way. He loved me, his parents liked me, Pa would make a fun granddad, Ma a cosy if eccentric granny, and I'd be married to a journalist. What more could I want?

That warm feeling stirred the tops of my thighs. I tugged Nick's hand. 'Let's go back to the house.'

By seven that Sunday evening, I was home, in the kitchen, watching Mum seated behind her sewing machine tacking a hem. She had a clutch of pins stuck between her lips, but she managed a 'Well?'

The sight of her, always at her machine, always working, dug up my buried affection for her. 'Sorry Mum. Nick's parents aren't millionaires.'

Mum spat out her pins and smiled at me. 'That's a relief. I was beginning to get all het up about meeting them. What's their house like?'

'Cramped. Smaller than this one.'

She beamed. 'And his mother?'

'She wears a funny old felt hat. In the house.' We looked at each other in a rare mother and daughter moment. I'd pleased my mother, which was a change, while she congratulated herself on being more smartly dressed than her immediate rival. For once there were no secrets between us, not really. Suddenly I wanted to confide in her. 'Nick's father lives in a caravan,' I blurted out.

'An artistic caravan?'

'Would that make a difference?'

'He must be a bohemian. Never mind. It's not as if you are settling with Nick for the rest of your life.'

During that summer, I spent more weekends in Nick's house than mine. My mother astonished me by suggesting he come on holiday with us. The self-catering cottage in Cornwall had three bedrooms but, in spite of squeaky floorboards, I shared his bed each night. I slept while pretending to sun bathe on the beach.

Nick didn't mention condoms and I was too nervous to ask. We'd done the safe period during the O level course in human biology. I'd passed the exam with a B grade so thought I knew all the answers. Why bother with unobtainable pills or nasty rubber things when all I had to do was count from the first day of my last period to the 14th day of my cycle, when the fertilized egg pops out of its shell, the ovary. I knew how to beat nature at its own game. Days 14, 15 and 16 were not safe. All the rest were.

So I didn't worry as the weeks passed, just kept counting the days until one day I couldn't ignore the facts any longer.

I'd been a fool. Since I'd met Nick, I'd been behaving as though I was in a fairy tale, one where the prince marries the princess and they live happily ever after.

Suddenly, I needed to grow up and face the birth of my baby. I promised myself I'd do that while I was living in this special home for girls like me.

Nine

In 1965, sixty-six out of every 1000 babies born were illegitimate. Despite the 1960s being dubbed the permissive society, there was little tolerance within the perfect family life for a pregnant, unmarried daughter. Many sought the shelter of a mother-and-baby home; many, like me, were forced into one by their parents.

The homes run by the Church of England were, in general, the ones least bound by rules or harsh discipline.

My diary confirms I was becoming philosophical about my predicament.

Wednesday 31 March
Off after lunch. Banished to the cosy arms of the Church and Mrs Clements. Be glad to get away from home. Nick rang and said he has an interview with the BBC. No details but it's cheered me up. Can't wait to see what the home is like and meet the other girls. Just as long as it's not horribly strict!

I sit in the back of the car, Mum and Dad up front, the atmosphere a mixture of woeful goodbyes and a reluctant relief at finding a solution to my problem. My mother, wearing her this-is-all-dreadful-but-it-can't-be-avoided face, remains silent.

Apart from Brownie camp, this is the first time I have been away from home on my own. I am nervous but excited. All my mother has discovered is that girls normally arrive at the home six weeks before their due date and leave six weeks after the birth. She hasn't used the word baby. Not once. As she sees it, my bump is a bubble which, with any luck, will burst before anyone notices it. I might be a burden, a social nuisance to be bundled away out of sight until I'm a more comfortable creature to live with, but the cause of this, my stigma, will be an everlasting secret.

I lean forward. 'Aren't I going to this home a bit early? You said six weeks before. That's not for several weeks.'

My mother's voice dismisses me. 'It's all arranged.'

My father says, 'This home is going to cost me a fortune.'

'How?' I ask, 'Is it going to be expensive? Isn't it all to do with the council or some other organisation? Why are we paying?'

My mother's tone is faint, distant, as if she doesn't want to voice the answer, doesn't want to admit she even knew it. 'This is a Church of England home. Those who can afford it are asked to pay.' She shifts in her seat and turns to stare out of the window, sending the temperature in the car down by several degrees. 'They've been most understanding.'

'Who have?'

'The committee who run the home.'

So I'm to be handed over to a committee. No doubt a collection of well-meaning people similar to Mrs Bird.

'Understanding to whom? Hardly to me as they've never met me.'

My mother's voice wobbles as if she's embarrassed. 'We negotiated special arrangements. They are taking you earlier than usual.'

I glance down at my clothed body. I still have a lap and although I'm fuller in the face, I haven't yet acquired that plump, complacent look I've noticed on women who are in the final weeks of pregnancy. 'Why?' I demand, 'are they making me an exception?'

'Honestly, Jane, can't you see? The point of us sending you away is that no one will find out.'

'Yes, but how am I a special case?'

My mother turns to face me. She's very pink and I can tell she doesn't want to say this at all. 'Mrs Bird agreed to be vague about your dates. She said you weren't sure.'

My turn to feel hot. How dare they make me out to be a simpleton or a liar? 'But I am. I know exactly when…'

'When the little creep seduced you?' My mother's voice is back to crude mode. 'You know exactly when he got you into this mess, is that what you want to say? You know the very moment, the very minute, when you could have put a stop to it?'

Her shock, at the fact that I did what she and dad did every other night, makes me want to laugh, if only to emphasise how absurd her attitude is. How I wish mum had talked to me properly about it all because I'd have told her that, instead of experiencing ecstatic bliss, I found it pretty boring, just a matter of letting Nick do what he seemed to want to do. On the other hand, maybe better not.

Like a toddler seeking her comfort blanket, I finger the soft cloth of my sleeve. My going away outfit is the blue dress my mother made. I like it. It's comfortable. So far, the sum total of my maternity clothes is another pair of larger black slacks with an elasticated waist and a smock, black again but with bright red roses splashed across the buttoned front. I found that in C&A's, sending up a quick prayer of thanks for the current fashion of full tops gathered into yokes. I packed very little because, apart from pants and bras and stockings, I couldn't think what else to take. Nighties, of course, and my old dressing gown. I bought new slippers.

I wonder what I'll wear when it becomes hot in the summer. And then it hits me. By the summer I won't be pregnant any more.

The home sent a list of stuff for the baby. It includes two dozen terry towelling nappies. I'll save up my pocket money to buy those. As for the rest, at least I can knit.

Unable to resist reminding my parents just what this car drive is all about, I add, 'I'll have plenty of time for knitting.'

My father keeps his comment to, 'Almost there.'

We are driving along Wimbledon High Street, busy with traffic and shoppers coming from the underground station. I notice a Woolworth's where I'll be able to buy cheap stockings. As we start up the hill, I roll down the window to get a clear picture, to note every detail of the place which is to be my prison. The shops give way to houses, semi-detached, similar to the one we live in. Maybe there will be more to take comfort in than I expected. We reach a junction, a meeting of the ways which has a nostalgic atmosphere with a cluster of larger houses, Victorian or Edwardian, I'm not sure, and several trendy boutiques and delicatessens.

My mother announces, 'This is called The Village. It's quite smart.'

We turn left into a wide road with chestnut trees planted on the pavement. The houses here are detached and grand. I crane my neck to see brick walls hiding front gardens. We pull up in front of a large house, Georgian style (maybe the real thing), with a panelled front door painted a shiny black. Two long windows, small square panes surrounded by white glossed woodwork, sit either side of the door and, on the first floor, four of the same sit either side of a bay window. It reminds me of an expensive dolls' house, the kind I coveted when I was a child. But a dolls' house is shut closed until the owner opens it. Am I to be shut up until let out? Still, as a hideaway for wayward girls, this is a luxury pad.

We get out of the car and walk through the white, iron-work gate. This is finally happening. I glance at Mum. Poor Mum. The house of her dreams, the house she'd love to live in. And here she is, waiting to be admitted with her shameful daughter.

The door is opened by a young woman with short, dark hair and blue eyes. Quite pretty but not very smiley. She's wearing a blue dress, with a navy elastic belt and a watch hanging upside down on her chest. A nurse. What's she doing here? She doesn't tell us her name but beckons us into a large, square hall.

Immediately I like the pale yellow walls and polished wooden floor. Cheerful. Not a dungeon at all. I begin to feel better, to think that maybe a new beginning isn't so far off the truth after all. I look up the wide staircase, no carpet but bannisters with a darkly polished hand-rail and white, painted spindles, until the treads turn and there is a stained-glass window, just pieces of coloured glass, no pictures as in a church, but beautiful.

I imagine I can inhale the sweet scent of lavender. That I am in fields of purple and sage green, in sun and warmth and calmness. I'm free and slim and good. I'm almost happy.

We sit on upright chairs with hard seats and straight backs. From somewhere above, a baby cries. I stiffen.

There's no smell of pink disinfectant but also there's no sense of a kettle always on the go, or the newspapers strewn across a table. No books or ironing waiting to be carried up. Just my small suitcase. Disappointment arrives. It's not like a real home after all.

Mum is still and tight lipped. Dad walks up and down the hallway, trying not to notice the statue of a woman dressed in blue robes set in a niche in the wall. The Virgin Mary.

I can hear Rita giggling. 'Must be the only blinking virgin in South London.'

Hell, no one told me You'd be here. I expected religion to come in somewhere, but I didn't expect to see the perfect woman every day. She has a right to be here though. A young expectant mother, unmarried and, like me, great with child. She is a symbol of virtue and love, while I am, it seems, a symbol of all that is wrong with the world today. At least that's what Mum is soon to tell the matron, Mrs Clements.

The opening of a door makes us all jump. A small, neat woman, middle-aged, dressed in a grey skirt and cardigan over a pale blouse comes out. 'I'm Mrs Clements, the Matron. Come in Jane. We'll have a little chat before you go up.'

In her office, with a desk, chairs, flowers, a bookcase and a settee, we sit opposite her like three schoolchildren. I fix my attention on the vase of flowers on her desk while Mrs Clements talks about the number of girls here, meals, the expected length of my stay and also explains I'll be able to go home for the day on Sundays. This shocks me. I don't want to go home, to go back, but since everyone seems to think it's the thing to do, I stay quiet. Quiet seems best.

Eventually my mother says, 'I'd like a word with Matron in private. Wait outside, Jane.'

Outside I behave badly (after all that's why I'm here) and press my ear to the door.

My mother's voice is strident. 'What I want to know is, what exactly you think of all these girls becoming pregnant?'

Matron's voice is clear. 'Dreadful.'

So that's that. No love at the home after all and I stick out my tongue at the Virgin.

'What will happen, exactly, when Jane has her…' my mother is silent for a moment, 'that is after,' a small cough, 'the baby is born?'

That word baby thrills me, even though I know it shouldn't. I can't help it. At last, even Mum admits it exists.

Mrs Clements' voice sounds guarded, as if she's treading water with her words. 'That depends on Jane.'

Definitely a good omen.

'How does it?' That from my father.

'On her decision about what she wants to do.'

'What on earth do you mean?' My mother's good manners have vanished in a desperate bid to show that she is the one to take decisions in our family. 'There's nothing for Jane to decide. The child will be adopted. That's what she's here for, to get the whole thing over and done with as simply as possible.'

Simply! My head fills with a black thundering, a huge, terrible cloud of hurt and dismay. My hand goes to the door handle. I'll stop this right now. I'll burst in and tell them I'm not stopping, not staying in this place where babies are handed out like Smarties. But I don't. To keep Mrs Clements on my side I must not be rude to her on my first day. I sit down, to stare at the Virgin as if she might give me the answers. Adopted? When did I agree to that? Fiona! She arranged for me to come here, so she must have had the adoption thing in mind all along. And I thought I could trust her. A great wave of hopelessness sweeps me up and dumps me on rocks. Fiona was my only hope, the one person who could have helped me. And my baby.

I feel like laughing and crying all at the same time. My mother must have been jubilant when Fiona told her about the home. I can imagine the scene.

'I know about these girls,' Fiona would have said. 'Jane's not the first one. There's a way of dealing with it, believe me. It can all be arranged.'

Here I am, happily going along with the idea of coming to the home because I thought it was being done to keep me and my baby safe. True, no one has promised forgiveness but, surely, presented with her first grandchild, my mother will relent? For don't all women love babies? Haven't I been brought up to believe that what every woman wants is a baby in the house?

Not my mother. My mother, who would have turned my baby into a bloody mess in a basin, still wants to get rid of it and she doesn't care how.

I can't cry. Or laugh. Just sit on my chair, pressing the knuckle of one hand into the palm of the other, muttering to the blue-gowned Lady, 'You're no better than all the rest, then. As for You-up-There, forget I ever spoke.' Miracles, I know, don't exist.

Five minutes later the door opens and the four of us are together again; me, my parents and the Virgin.

'There's one thing about this dreadful business,' my father says to my mother. 'You do meet some pleasant people.'

That's all right then. Mrs C meets with their approval, so I can be left behind. No bad influences on me here! He gestures towards the stairs. 'You take Jane up.' As if I'm not here.

I don't care about being ignored. I have nothing to say to them, to these two people who can so callously dispose of my baby without even mentioning it to me. What I have to say is clearly of no interest to them. Because what I have to say is, I'm not doing it. I want my baby even if its father doesn't. Whatever you might want or tell me to do, I'm doing things my way now and that doesn't include giving my baby away to the most suitable bidder.

The stairs rise shallow and wide. At the turn in the staircase, we stand to let a woman, heavy with child, pass. Hanging onto the rail for support, she treads carefully. We are about the same height. I can smell the scent of shampoo from her head, but I don't look her in the face. Wearing a navy pleated dress, even with her ankles swollen, she radiates mature calm, a sure sense of being in control, of not being in a mess. Surely, she doesn't belong in a mother-and-baby home? Surely, she knows better? I stare at her bump, this much too physical fact of life, this empathy with my own condition. I flush and push ahead of my mother, so she can't see my face. The placid pregnant woman has shamed me more than I've shamed myself. I dread meeting her.

'The left room is for the mums-to-be,' Matron told us. 'The bed next to the door is free. Karen had her baby last night.'

Sounded so cosy, that, so straightforward. Karen had her baby last night. Inside this house, babies are not abominations, to be ignored, wished away, to be destroyed. They cry and are rocked and fed.

I wonder what Karen is like. No furtive arrangements for her. No deception about what she might do with her baby. Perhaps guilt is absent in the mothers' room. Perhaps the Virgin does her stuff and forgives us after our labours. But then, and a terrible thought occurs to me, perhaps the other girls are happy with the adoption arrangement. Perhaps they don't want their babies, don't want them to muck up their lives for them. Perhaps I'm the one to be different, still the odd one out. I don't belong here. I'm not going to get along with them. It's not at all as I expected. I was making it up. Now I know, I want to run.

We are on the landing. A lost soul, I push open the door on the left.

119

The bedroom is spacious and bright. A long room with two windows on one side, one at the end. There are two rows of three narrow beds covered with green and blue checked rugs. Each bed has a bedside locker, with a reading lamp, on one side and a chest of drawers on the other.

I put my case by the bed near to the door and wait. I don't know what to say to my mother. Random thoughts run through my head, feelings of regret, pain, sorrow but most of all of being let down by the one person who should have loved me enough to want to help me. I know I've let her down. I shouldn't be in this house of shame and neither should I have brought this on my mother.

My heart is hurting, confusion strangling my throat, my hands are hot and cold at once and my legs want to throw me onto the bed so I can bury my face in the pillow and cry and cry. I want to tell mum I'm sorry, that if I had the chance I'd do things differently. I want to be friends with her.

But she doesn't want to be friends with me. She glances around the room and then back at me, desperate to get away. As long as she stands in this room, this haven for wicked girls, the stain in their lives will seep through to her life, will leave an indelible mark on her, on her best coat, on her gloves. Her devotion to keeping herself respectable is stronger than her love for her only daughter.

Right up to the last minute, I'm hoping mum will change her mind and take me home with her. She cannot abandon me.

'Quite pleasant, isn't it?' she says, as if she's assessing an hotel room in which she is to take a short break. 'It's a nice number, six. You'll soon make friends.'

'I thought you didn't like me mixing with girls like this. Girls who are no better than they should be.'

'I expect one or two will come from backgrounds like yours. From families who care enough to arrange all this for them.'

As if I'm being given a special treat.

'I'll say goodbye then.' At last there's a tremor in my mother's voice which, contrarily, makes me feel better. She's hurting too.

I make my voice sound firm, while all the time I'm thinking, *She's leaving me here, then. She's going through with it. With this scheme to hide me away until she can be proud of me again.*

I say, 'I'll see you on Sunday.' What more is there to say? I love you? I'll miss you? No. I'll miss my home, even though it has become a battlefield. I'll miss us eating together, in spite of the silence, each of us resenting, regretting. I'll miss my room, with my childhood books, even though I am no longer a child. But, although it hurts me to know it, I won't miss you, mother. I know I've done wrong. I do feel guilty, at least of making you unhappy. But you've made me feel that all of this mess is solely my fault. I can't be responsible for your reactions, for your apparent lack of love for me, the pushing me away from you as though I am a leper. I think I understand why you're doing it, but surely you've some love left for me? Enough to be kind. Enough to care for the health of your grandchild.

I'm hoping to find peace in this new home of mine, the peace to allow me to come to some conclusion about the future of my child.

I kiss her on her cheek and smell face powder with a trace of fried bacon.

My mother swallows and her jaw tenses. We both need to cry but neither of us wants to be the first to show weakness. 'Go on,' I say. 'Dad'll be waiting. I'll write.'

'He'll pick you up at twelve on Sunday then?'

'Sunday. Yes.'

My mother hesitates. She rolls her top lip in and blinks hard. 'You know,' she begins, blinking faster, 'we're doing this for the best.'

I want to challenge her with best for whom? but I don't have the energy. I want her gone. If this is to be a new beginning, let it start quickly.

Mum's determined to have her final say. 'You know we love you. You know we're doing this because we love you, don't you?'

I don't but what's one more lie? I put my arms round her neck and kiss her again. 'Yes, Mum, I know. It's OK. Don't worry.'

That's it. My mother has gone.

Ten

Alone, I pat the swell of my stomach and allow myself to feel a twinge of excitement. Just a twinge, nothing more, but it's enough to banish the tears. The sun comes around the corner of the house, shining directly through the end window. With any luck I'll be sitting in that garden in May, a lady-in-waiting, calm, rounded and maybe even a little bit happy.

On tiptoe, like a trespasser, I walk the length of the room between the beds.

The locker next to mine boasts an alarm clock, a red notebook, a sharpened pencil and a framed photograph. Tidy and orderly. I guess a page of the book has a list beginning with two dozen nappies but even I am not a bad enough girl to pry. I pick up the photograph. A happy family, a mum and dad and four youngsters. The elder sister, taller than the other children, dark haired, is holding a baby. She signals responsibility from her plain face, love from her smile. In a flash I imagine myself as part of that family, with an elder sister to look out for me, to stop me mucking up my life.

Don't do this, don't let it get to you. You haven't mucked up, not yet, not totally.

On the top of the locker by the window is a cloth bag with knitting needles sticking out. I am looking forward to being able to sit and knit in peace without my mother sighing heavily and telling me that she doesn't know how it will all end. As far as I am aware, it can end only one way. It's the middle bit I can't fathom.

Another locker has face and hand cream plus a huge pot of something called Anti-Stretch Cream. Anti-stretch what? Will I be brave enough to ask the owner what exactly she does with it? Will I be so friendly with another pregnant girl that we'll swap aches and pains, stories and jokes? The next locker has a library book with one of those romantic illustrations on it, a young girl in a summer frock gazing into the eyes of Mr Tall-Dark-and-Handsome, Jane Eyre 1960s style. Someone who still believes in romance, whatever it has done to her.

The final locker, the one opposite mine, is stacked high with tapes. These I do investigate. The Rolling Stones, the Beatles, Billy Fury, Elvis. Whoever sleeps in this bed has the lot. The cassette entitled Dancing Beat makes me smile. Some clumsy dancers we'll make.

I'm unpacking, T-shirts and underclothes in the chest of drawers, writing pad and pen in my locker cupboard, library book, *damn, I should have left that behind,* when a girl comes in. With her freckled face, unruly ginger curls and eyes enlarged by national health specs she's exactly the kind of girl I expected to find here. Noting her grubby jumper and faded jeans, I let myself take on my mother's prejudices. This girl is from a deprived background. This girl, who looks too young, has been taken advantage of. This is the kind of girl I am not.

She grins at me. Actually grins as if she were happy. 'You new?'

'Yes.'

'When's your baby due?'

I hesitate. I don't want anyone to know I'm a special case. I'm in that home to be the same as all the others. I want to fit in. I need a place which wants me. I'm going to rely on friends in this new life of mine. A small white lie. 'Middle of May. When's yours due?'

She laughs.

Heavens! A laughing matter.

'I've had mine.'

I look at the place I've been avoiding, the place I've learnt shouldn't be there. At her bump. Which isn't there. I blush with stupidity. 'Do you sleep next door then?'

'Not yet. My baby's in hospital. Its arm got broke when it came out. It'll be here in another week or so.'

I can't think of anything to say. For the first time it occurs to me that this baby business might not be as straightforward as I expect.

Her face creases in a smile. 'My name's Tina. What's yours?'

Tina so suited her. I grin back. 'Jane.'

She walks to her locker, the one at the far end of the room by the window, and snatches at the knitting. 'I'm learning. Bit difficult.'

'I'll help you.'

The grin widens. 'See you later then.'

I nod, already feeling better. I'm beginning to agree with my mother. Being here is for the best. I decide to write a letter home. Posting it will give me something to do tomorrow afternoon. If we're allowed to go out. No one has said.

Dear Mum,

    I'm just writing to say don't worry about me. I'll be fine. I've already met another girl who is very nice. Her baby is in hospital with a broken arm. I didn't know babies could break their arms. It's very quiet here and I can have time to think. Don't worry. I won't do anything without letting you know. I don't want to upset you any more than I have already. I wish things would straighten themselves out and then they wouldn't look so bleak…

A tall girl with dark hair cut in a bob and a huge bump under a smock patterned with blue flowers interrupts me.

'I'm Sylvia. You must be Jane. I've been sent to get you. Lunch is ready.' She opens the door of the locker with the photo on it, takes out a comb and runs it through her hair. As her arm moves, her smock swirls like a swathe of bluebells in a spring breeze.

So the one with a proper family, sleeping in the bed next to me, is called Sylvia. She's friendly enough.

'I'd come soon before the gannets eat the lot.' And Sylvia leaves as abruptly as she'd arrived.

Bleak? With a sudden certainty I'm about to enjoy myself, I tear my letter to my mother in half, promising myself I'll write a different letter after I've been here a day or two. Once I have something interesting to tell her.

'What's your name?'

'Do you have a bloke?'

'When are you due?'

'Giving it up for adoption, are you?'

'Sylvia's not are you, Sylvia? Sylvia's getting a job as a mother's help. Then she can keep it.'

The brown-haired girl in the blue-flowered smock smiles as she eats for two, her plate loaded with mince, mashed potatoes, carrots and cabbage.

I feel bad staring at her, behaving like a visitor in a zoo of strange animals from a distant planet. It won't be long before I'll turn into a similar creature, with a huge bump under my dress. But will I be happily eating for two, ready to welcome my baby into my new world?

We eat in the room at the front of the house, leading off the left hand side of the hall. It is a large enough room to double as a sitting room and a dining room.

This end of the room has French windows overlooking the garden and the space is filled with a long table covered with one of those plastic-looks-like-linen cloths printed with a trendy flower design. A door leads to the kitchen.

It's a bright room, full of light and colour with a sense of previous meals. Brown toast made under the grill, hot milky coffee, onion gravy over crisp Yorkshire pudding and apples softened under a pie crust, melted butter on hot toast. Or am I imagining it?

After pudding, treacle tart and custard, tea is served in a huge brown pot which brings a burst of amused happiness to me as it's the twin of the tea-pot my Seaside Gran used. For years of summers I have been sitting round her long table, drinking tea. I begin to feel at home. Better than home. I am contented for the first time in months.

It's the strongest tea I have ever drunk. One or two mothers ladle sugar in theirs, making me wonder whether this baby stuff is more tiring than I thought! Certainly, the mothers more or less drank their tea in silence while it was the mothers-to-be who chatted constantly, filling me in on the routine of my new home.

I'm told there are twelve of us altogether. Quickly I have become part of them. Apart from Tina and myself in the ante-natals room, there are four with bumps. Six girls have their babies and Tina. Tina is very quiet, as if she is wishing she had her baby with her.

One girl called Georgie, blonde, with a high pony tail, asks me, 'Do you come from London? Most of us do but I'm American.' Her accent was straight from a US sit-com.

Georgie is the first person from the States I've ever met, so I'm intrigued. As politely as I can I ask her how she's ended up in the home.

She shrugs. 'I was working here as an au pair. The father of my child was the woman's husband and he couldn't pack me off here quickly enough.' She pauses. 'At least he can pay the bill.'

Her words take me back to my journey, with my father complaining about the cost of the home.

'Have some more tea,' offers Sylvia. 'I made it. Your turn soon. You'll either be on kitchens or cleaning every morning.'

Cleaning! Bang goes my anticipated rest cure. 'What do we clean?'

Tina points to a cork notice board on the wall by the fireplace. 'A rota goes up.' She laughs. 'Not the mothers. They're too busy with their babies.'

With their babies. How long will it take this casual way of referring to our great sin to become familiar?

The woman we passed on the stairs leans forward. 'Did Mrs Clements tell you we have cookery classes on Tuesday evening with Mrs Groom and sewing on Thursdays?' She boasts a straight row of brilliant white teeth. 'Other than that, your time is your own. I'm Deborah, by the way. Known as Debbie.'

The name suits her. She seems to me slightly older, more mature than the others. How on earth did she get herself into such a mess? Obviously human frailty respects no one.

I ask her who Mrs Groom is.

'The cook. Good plain food. The next day, we eat the food we make,' she continues, 'so I hope you can cook already.' This was almost an order but tempered with a smile.

I look at her smooth skin, her clean hands with round, short nails. Smart, classy.

'Debbie's a midwife,' Tina whispers. 'A sister at a hospital. She's a bit bossy but kind really.'

I'm even more amazed. A midwife who gets pregnant. So being a sinner is not necessarily the result of ignorance.

There are still six empty chairs. 'Where are those girls?' I'm becoming bolder.

'The mums are still feeding,' Debbie tells me. 'You'll learn, once you're a mum, that your requirements don't come first.'

Once you're a mum. Again, I know I haven't yet become reconciled that I will be a mum. I feel myself colour. From what? Embarrassment? Shame? No, no longer shame. Already that has left me.

I'm surrounded by smiles and laughter, chattering mouths and fragments of tantalising information. The others are treating me as if they are pleased to have me here, as if they want me to be glad I've arrived. I don't dwell on the difference in atmosphere between this meal and the previous day's supper time at home, with the intimidating silence, the implied accusations, the recriminations. I've only been a resident of the home for an hour and already I'm pushing away the memory of my other home to the back bench.

Eleven

In May 1963, opening a fundraising fete for a mother-and-baby home, Margaret Thatcher was quoted as saying, 'It is our job to help these mothers and babies with kindness and firmness.'

I had already received the firmness. I was reassured and happy to discover the kindness.

Sylvia, explaining she's on kitchens until after breakfast tomorrow, carries the dirty china out to the kitchen.

The rest of us move to the sitting room end, settling ourselves around a fireplace, on the sofa or one of the three armchairs. There's a low coffee table scattered with magazines and a television set. Georgie offers me a cigarette.

I shake my head. 'No, thanks.'

She grins. 'Never?'

I shrug. 'I've never fancied it but then I've never been able to afford it.' I'm about to add 'My boyfriend does though' when I realise I'm not ready to talk about Nick yet, but already, he doesn't fit into this new world of mine. Like my mother, he's gone.

Sticking her head back round the door, Sylvia calls, 'Mrs Groom says, is the new girl on a salt-free diet?' She looks at me. 'Well, new girl?'

'Not as far as I know,' I say. 'When does that happen?'

Rachel, a mother-to-be, must be in her early thirties, responds. 'I've got slightly raised blood pressure. Caused by all that tension worrying about my father. If this baby doesn't arrive on time, drastic measures will be called for.' She laughs at this, blue eyes shining.

Tina says, 'You mean slipping on a piece of soap all the way from the top of the stairs to the bottom?'

'So that's a no then.' Sylvia returns to the kitchen.

Trying not to stare at Rachel's bump, I ask her when her baby's due.

'In about three weeks or so.'

Again, Rachel looks older than me, but then they probably all are except Tina. 'What's the problem with your father?' As if I don't have a problem with mine. Or rather he has a problem with me.

'He doesn't know where I am.' She gazes at me as if this is the most normal situation in the world.

'But how…'

Rachel pulls a face. 'I left my flat up north and came down here. My aunt arranged it all. She knows.'

'You are both keeping it a secret from your father?'

'Have to. At least Aunt Grace understands her brother. He'd probably kill me.'

And here she is looking so calm.

'Mind you,' Rachel finishes, 'If this baby doesn't push itself out sooner rather than later, I'll have to help it.'

I'm keen to absorb all the knowledge on offer. 'How?'

'I've heard that a bottle of castor oil does the trick.'

Deborah overhears the remark. 'Painful though.'

'Less so than dealing with my father,' is Rachel's answer. 'Your parents brought you here didn't they?' she asks me.

'Yes. Did someone come with you?'

'Gosh, no. Even my aunt doesn't want to be seen with me.'

The idea that someone is so independent they can hide themselves away from their own father is a revelation for me. 'What exactly did you say to your father?'

'That I was going abroad. He expects me back the week after the baby's due date, hence the slight panic.'

Someone in a trickier situation than I am. Another good reason to be in the home. I'm learning to be sympathetic to others' troubles.

Rachel whispers, 'I expect your parents are all right about it.'

I can't help wondering how long it will be before I can tell the truth. Because telling the truth will mean betraying my mother, showing her not as she really is, but what she has become since I let her down so badly. I'm not sure, any more, what her real feelings are. Not since she's abandoned me. 'Not really, but at least I can go home on Sundays.'

'Not this Sunday,' Debbie says. 'No going home on the first Sunday. It's to let you settle in. Didn't Mrs Clements tell you?'

I feel a bit of a fool. 'At the end of our chat with her, my mum asked me to wait outside.'

There's a brief silence and then Tina says, 'You didn't say if you'd got a fella.'

I might as well tell more or less the truth. 'I've got a boyfriend.'

'Is he the father?'

'Of course.'

'Is your bloke standing by you?'

I gulp a mouthful of tea. I'm not sure of the answer. When my mouth is empty I tell her, 'He says he loves me.'

Georgie is cynical. 'Just what that man said when he was seducing me.'

I am too young all over again. Innocent. Ignorant. I don't ask how many of my new friends have the father of their baby standing by them, since I have a hunch the answer will be at the least embarrassing. I'm learning that, in this world of unmarried mothers, the truth is often painful.

I begin to suspect I might be better without my parents looking after me and without Nick standing by me. If I were on my own, I could take my own decisions, with no one telling me what to do. Or what to think. Or whom to love. I tried to see myself without Nick, even without my parents, like some of the other girls. For a second, I imagined myself as free and easy as Georgie or as sensible as Sylvia, finding a job in a home which would welcome me.

Subversive thoughts. Much too revolutionary for the first few days away from my parents.

I hear a baby cry and I remember. I'm not on my own. Soon there'd be two of us. Because of Nick. Nick's involved in my future whether I like it or not. This baby means I am destined to be chained to Nick for better or for worse.

Later, I phone home.

Clatter as the pennies drop.

'Mum, it's me.'

'Jane? Where are you?'

'In a phone box. Over the road from the home.'

'Outside? In the street?'

'Of course.'

'Why?'

'To tell you I'm not allowed home on the first Sunday.'

'I wasn't told that.' Now she sounds cross.

I try to sound matter-of-fact. 'It's something to do with settling in.'

'How ridiculous.'

'I'd better go.' I hang up, close the door of the telephone box behind me and cross the road.

That night, before going to sleep, I make a few notes in my diary. A midwife who's got herself into the same trouble as me. An American who's escaped the States only to end up in an institution. One girl who is so grown-up she can get a job as a mother's help. And yet another one who can't even tell her father. All of which makes me feel better about myself, less of a criminal. Not quite as indecent as my parents told me I am. I'm beginning to relax, to feel part of something, something I don't fully understand yet but something I want to become familiar with. I long to learn all about the other girls, as much as they are clearly interested to learn about me.

My time here will be interesting, if challenging. Certainly, it will be different.

I sleep well and for breakfast demolish two bowls of cornflakes and two pieces of honeyed toast.

'You'll need that,' says Rachel, as she clears away 'You're on stairs.' And she nods towards a list on the notice board.

I read: 'Jane – Stairs: scrub, rinse and dry all stairs from the hall to the 2nd floor.'

An April Fool's joke? I think not.

I need a prayer or two to manage that! We gather together, sitting closely as both the mothers and the ante-natals attend prayers. The babies were fed at six this morning and shouldn't need attention until ten.

After a short reading from the New Testament, Mrs Clements prays for better family relations and we all recite the Our Father. Then she hands out the post. Tina and I are the only two not to have a letter.

Tina displays her usual common sense. 'My lot don't write. Some of them can't.'

I hold my breath just for a moment to control my emotions and then admit, 'I'm not expecting my mother to write.'

'What about your bloke?'

I manage a laugh. 'He can write but he doesn't. Not anymore. Does your bloke write?'

'Got to be joking.'

'I'd better start those stairs. Where do I find the bucket and…?'

'Scrubbing brush,' Rachel calls out. 'In the scullery on the far side of the kitchen. Detergent is under the sink. Wash today, polish tomorrow.'

There are two flights, right the way to the top of the house, with me kneeling on the wooden treads with no soft kneeling pad. Immediately, I realise it would have been better to begin at the top as, now I'm moving up the risers, I'm kneeling on the damp, scrubbed treads. My back starts to ache by the turn in the first flight. I tell myself the exercise is strengthening my back muscles. Ready for when I have to push my baby into this world.

By half-past ten I'm exhausted, wishing I didn't have to ever go up the stairs, let alone clean them. I sit in the lounge, drinking my hot chocolate and helping myself to another biscuit from the trolley. Garibaldis, or squashed fly they're called, with the currants pressed into the surface of the mixture.

Girls drift in as they finish their chores with a couple of mothers who've finished feeding early. I get on with my knitting.

Tina sits next to me on the couch, watching me. 'Shall I fetch mine?' she suggests.

'I'll help you. I've only got to cast off and I've finished this pram set.' I hold up the little coat, hanging on the needle. 'Then I'll have to buy some more wool. Trouble is I haven't got much money.'

Tina looks at me, clearly surprised. 'What about the leftovers from your board money?'

Now it's my turn to be surprised. 'What board money?'

'National Assistance Board. You ought to have about three pounds fifty left after they've deducted your money for here.'

I don't want to offend Tina, but I have to sort this out. 'Your father doesn't pay your fees?'

Tina chortles, her face full of smiles and easiness. 'My old man wouldn't pay any fees for me. He don't care if he never sees me again. Good riddance to you, girl, that's what he said the day I left for this place. Good riddance to him that's what I say.'

I'm confused. Is there one rule for Tina and another for me and how did the National Assistance Board come into it?

Tina must sense my ignorance because she says much too kindly, 'How are you paying for this place?'

'My father is paying. He says…'

Tina gives a low whistle. 'Your parents must be loaded.'

After lunch, I walk across the road to the phone box, hoping I can persuade Nick to see me, maybe help out with a bit of money. Debbie has told me we're allowed out all afternoon as long as we tell Mrs Clements. We can miss tea, that's our choice, but have to return in time for supper. I have nowhere to go to until I get some pocket money from Dad next weekend.

The phone seems to ring for a long time. Eventually, 'Hello.' It's Ma's voice.

I feed the coins into the box. I have no idea what to say to her.

'Hello? Who's there?'

'It's Jane. I was hoping to speak to Nick.'

'He's at work.' Of course. I was so keen to ask him what he thinks about adoption I forgot the most important thing of all. He has a job. He is working for me and the baby. My euphoria is short-lived.

'He hates it.' Ma's voice is bitter.

Does she loathe me so much? 'What does he hate?' is all I can manage.

'That dreadful place you've made him go to.'

'I didn't…'

'Just to look after that bastard of yours. Sure it's his are you?'

I slam down the phone. My legs are trembling, my heart thumping. I feel sick. I need tea and company. Only just remembering to look right and left, I cross the road and take cover in the mother-and-baby home.

On Saturday morning, after prayers, Mrs Clements hands me a letter. The envelope is in my mother's handwriting. I open it with mixed feelings. A letter brings my mother into the sitting room, with me sitting here at peace. Even if I have a sore back with all the washing and polishing.

> *Dear Jane,*
>
> *This is just to say we are thinking of you and hope you are settling down. I'm sure some of the other girls will be quite pleasant. There are one or two things we haven't had time to discuss. We are disappointed not to be seeing you this Sunday but we'll see you the following Sunday.*
>
> *Your father will pick you up at twelve. We are looking forward to having the chance to talk things over.*
>
> *Your loving mother.*

My heart sinks. The picture of our dining room hangs in my head with its stark, formal furniture, so different from the table here. And what's there to talk over? Haven't we talked over everything already? What's new? I fold the letter back into its envelope, ready to tuck it at the back of my locker drawer.

Saturday is more relaxed. No chores. Some girls go down the hill to the main shops in Wimbledon. My tube of toothpaste is empty and my soap, in its blue plastic box has dwindled to a scrap. Soon, I'm going to have to shop. But with what? In my purse I have the remainder of last week's pocket money. Half-a-crown.

◆ ◆ ◆

'Jane, will you walk with me to church?' Debbie asks me.

It's Sunday morning and we're eating breakfast. Debbie is sitting across the table from me.

'Church?' My voice is an astounded squeak.

Debbie puts down her cup. 'Didn't Mrs Clements tell you that either?'

'Sung communion but you don't have to take it.' A no-nonsense comment from Sylvia, who is next to me.

I turn to her. 'You mean, if we do want to take communion, we just walk up? With our bumps?'

There's a gale of laughter from everyone else. I hear, 'Shy are you?' 'Shocked, then?' and 'Of course.'

I'm amazed. 'Don't they mind? The congregation I mean.'

'Got no choice have they?' Tina is clearly the pragmatic one. 'This is a Church of England home. We have to go, and they have to have us.' She sounds braver than she looks capable of being. 'They give us coffee afterwards.'

'Coffee?' More and more of everyday life. The kind of life I thought I didn't deserve any more.

'Made by the good ladies of the parish,' says someone and there's more laughter.

Not only am I amazed that we have to go to church but that we can present ourselves to the good congregation of St

John the Divine, who will sit and watch as we walk to the altar. My recently developed guilty conscience at keeping things back from my mother drives me across the road once more to the telephone box. I press the receiver to my ear, waiting for her to pick up. Then, 'Mum, just something else to tell you.'

'Hurry up, I'm off to church.'

'So am I. We all go to communion. Ten o'clock.'

Her voice sounds strained. 'I'll speak to Mrs Clements tomorrow and put a stop to it.'

'We have to go. All of us. Leave it, mum.'

Then, 'I can't think of anyone we know over there but do try to avoid talking to too many people. We'll discuss all this next week. Maybe you'll be able to talk things over sensibly once you've been in that home for a couple of weeks.'

Twelve

If a minister be persuaded that any person who presents himself to be a partaker of the holy Communion ought not to be admitted thereunto by reason of ... other grave sin and open sin without repentance... provided that in case of grave and immediate scandal to the Congregation the Minister shall not admit that person...

The Book of Common Prayer,
According to the use of the Church of England.

Certainly, I was guilty of giving immediate scandal to the congregation of any self-respecting church and, according to the 1662 Common Prayer Book, I should be afforded an opportunity for interview by the minister before he refused me the sacrament. No one suggested that such procedure was necessary. We were all expected to attend church, whether we were communicants or not.

◆ ◆ ◆

On my first Sunday, we walk from the home to the church of St John the Divine in a crocodile. Not just like school though since we can chat but still no running! Running is something most of us can't manage and we're not late. No one is allowed to stay behind.

'What about Catholics?' I ask. Catholics were excused prayers at both schools I'd attended and that sticks in my mind.

Tina giggles. 'This is a Church of England home. No Romans here.'

Inside the church a lady wearing a hat hands out hymn books, the green ones, denoting the church is high church and will probably use the 1662 service, which I love.

We sit at the back; two pews of us. I sit next to Debbie.

It's such a long time since I've been to a service, I need to find my place in the Prayer Book, but then I gaze around me, still amused I'm playing a part in a seemingly inappropriate scene. The church is full, with the obligatory pew of elderly ladies at the front and then rows of families, mums, dads and children of all ages. Some infants have books to look at, older ones are reading small red books which I recognize as the ones given out in preparation for confirmation. One or two girl teenagers are virtuously marking their places in white prayer books. No one in the congregation stares at us, no one tut-tuts or shakes their heads at us or asks us to leave because we are not worthy to eat at their table.

I decide not to even think whether I'd be in this mess if I hadn't left off going to church, but instead pray that the girls in this congregation do their rebelling without taking it to extremes. I guess, however understanding of us the congregation is, none would want their own daughters becoming unmarried mothers. I'm admiring the flowers, a huge display of lilies in a pedestal near the font, when the organist strikes the first note and the choir enters.

I turn to the first hymn, Ye Choirs of New Jerusalem. A good tune. I can do with a bit of holy joy.

Later, after confessing our sins, four of us, me, Debbie, Georgie and one of the mums whose name I don't yet know, make our way up to the Communion rail. I'm quite comfortable as my bump isn't huge but I can't imagine how I'll feel in a few weeks' time. I manage to kneel at the communion rail and get myself back on my feet without making a fool of myself. I am forgiven my sins and am cleansed.

After the service we all troop down some stairs to the crypt.

'Coffee?' A bright voiced woman beams at me and offers a plate of biscuits.

I hold in my bump. I'm wearing only a cardigan over my blue dress. 'Me? Would I like coffee?'

'We always have parish coffee after the service. Are you new?'

I nod and take a biscuit but can't look at her, not properly.

She pours coffee into a willow patterned cup. 'Milk and sugar?'

'Just milk, thank you.' Very polite I am. It's the least I can do.

'Are you managing your extra pint a day?' The woman laughs as she hands me the hot, milky coffee. 'For your baby. It was an extra pint a day in my days. I don't expect things have changed that much.'

I swallow coffee. How hard it is to be normal. I want to ask, 'Am I, after all, just a woman having a baby? Not a freak? Not a curse on your lovely church?' What I do say is, 'I haven't been to a clinic yet, so I don't know.'

She takes that statement in her stride, no furious blinking or sly grimace. 'You'll be going to the Nelson.'

'The Nelson?'

'The local hospital. That's where you all go from the home.'

There it is, out in the open. I am from the home, labelled but not, it seems, stigmatized. Not outlawed. I think, here goes. 'Don't you mind, here at St John's? Don't you mind having us at your service?'

The woman looks at me as if no one has asked her that before. As if it has never occurred to her to think maybe, as sinners, we shouldn't be welcome. She flushes faintly and I'm beginning to think I've blundered when she uses an extra bright voice to say, 'It's no use crying over spilt milk, is it?'

I agree it isn't.

Back at the home, breakfast is cleared away and there are no chores to do on a Sunday.

We cluster on the comfy old sofa or settle in chairs in a semi-circle. Voices chatter, music comes from the radio, the warm scents of toast and hot milk mix with the enticing smell of lunch cooking. We knit, read or just rest. Since I have to wait for my next pocket money before I can buy more wool, I read a woman's magazine.

There's an article headed, Bottle or Breast?

I tell the others, thinking it might lead to an interesting discussion on the topic but Tina, as usual, puts me right.

'Got no choice. Can't feed them ourselves since they're going off to their new mums, so it's bottles here, like it or lump it.'

That evening, those of us who don't yet have babies to feed, watch a programme on the ancient black and white TV about teenage pregnancy. Not that we are all teenagers. Midwife Debbie is happy to tell us she is almost thirty. Rachel admits to twenty-five. Georgie says she has to be twenty-one to be an au pair but refuses to answer more questions. I guess Sylvia is older, maybe about thirty, because she intends to keep her baby and to look for a post as a home help. It seems I am the only one who fits the profile of being an irresponsible teenager. Except Tina. Her ginger curls and toothy smile remind me of a character in the *Beano*, but I remind myself she has a child in hospital. I daren't ask her. Is it possible she's under the age of consent? Maybe the father is the same age.

The television commentator maintains that six teenage couples out of every forty are having faithful sex. Faithful but, nevertheless, immoral. They are doing wrong. With dreadful consequences. Bringing shame on all their houses.

Even if the programme doesn't make me feel better about being pregnant, sitting amongst my new friends, I don't feel threatened. I'm starting to believe I am not as wicked as my parents make out. I am, in one way, the odd one out. I am the only girl who admits to being in touch with the father of her baby, even though I haven't heard from Nick. Not even a letter.

◆ ◆ ◆

On Wednesday morning, Sue, the nurse comes into the lounge as soon as matron leaves after prayers. 'Jane, can we have a word? I don't seem to have any clinic notes for you.'

I blush. 'That's because I've not been to one. Not yet.'

'You should be going twice a month by now. I'll ring the hospital. You'd better go with the others this morning.'

We take the same route as we did on Sunday but walk past the turning for the church, over a bridge and across the main road. The Nelson Hospital is smaller than I expected. In the clinic we sit on benches until our names are called. We are all addressed as 'Mrs'. When my turn comes, I say, 'I'm Miss…'

The nurse is firm. 'All our ladies are known as Mrs. It saves the embarrassment for the real mothers.'

Obediently, I get undressed and lie on the couch waiting.

The young doctor palpates my bump and then announces, 'Is it possible you have your dates wrong?'

'I suppose it might be.' Could it be? I count on my fingers but can't be sure. 'My doctor told me the baby is due at the beginning of June,' I venture.

'That's all right then. Plenty of time.'

'For what?'

'Your baby is still lying head up. It will either settle down later or we'll have a breach on our hands.'

We wait until we have all seen the doctor and go home together. On the way, I ask Debbie for her advice.

'Don't worry,' she tells me. 'It's early days yet. If they have to, they'll turn it. You might feel a bit sore, but it's worth the trouble.'

By the end of the week, Tina's baby is restored to her and they move into the mothers' bedroom. We have a new girl called Julie, who tells us she is from the Elephant and Castle and lives near to the Kray twins. It doesn't seem to bother her. 'They're OK. At least they look after their old mum. Which is more than some do.'

I am bold enough to ask her if she is keeping her baby.

She laughs, a deep in the belly chuckle. 'You gotta be joking. My old man told me to get the hell out of it and not go back till I was rid of it.'

The following Sunday my father picks me up, as agreed, just before twelve and drives me home in silence. In the kitchen, my mother is battling with serving up the pork, roast potatoes, greens, with gravy and apple sauce. I set the table in the dining room, carefully putting each piece of cutlery in its correct place, nice and genteel.

It's too much to hope things would stay pleasantly domestic. The first course is eaten more or less in silence, if you don't count the remarks my father makes about the lack of easy conversation with his staff and how he wonders how much of this dreadful thing has got around or my mother's complaints about how the meat isn't as tender as it should be. Not a word spoken directly to me. Remembering last week's Sunday lunch with the chortles of glee as the gravy is poured as thickly as that morning's porridge, I tell myself I should have stayed at the home.

'We have to help with the lunch on Sundays,' I try. 'Mrs Groom comes in to put the meat in the oven, but we have to prepare the vegetables and take the joint out when it's ready and serve it up as she has gone home by then.'

'I thought her name was Mrs Clements,' my mother observes, dryly, as if we are talking about a robot rather than another woman.

'Mrs Groom is the cook. We have cookery and sewing lessons once a week.'

The mention of sewing catches my mother's interest. 'Does Mrs Groom sew as well?'

'There's a sweet little old lady called Mrs Angel who does that. She is too,' I chatter on, 'an angel I mean. So patient. D'you know one of the girls can't even knit. I'm teaching her...'

'I could do that,' my mother announces. 'I'd be just the right kind of person to set those girls a good example.'

My father makes a grunting noise, like a camel who doesn't want to give a ride at the zoo. 'You wouldn't want to waste your time on those girls. They're nothing better than a lot of tarts.'

Under the table, I clench my fingers into my palm. Does my father really believe he's sent me to live with women who are that low? Does he believe that of me, his only daughter? If he does, is that my fault? I'm beginning to think it isn't, that whatever my mother or father think of me is because of their prejudices.

Nevertheless, I'm not prepared to let a demeaning comment like that pass. My loyalty to my new friends is worth defending. 'Actually, one of the mothers-to-be is a midwife and one comes from America. One is going to keep her baby and get a job as a mother's help. Maybe to a father who's on his own.'

My mother has the answer to that. 'She's no fool. She's hoping he'll marry her.'

'The only man who'll have her.' My father looks up from his food. His face is wearing its sour expression. 'Which is more than any decent man will do for you.'

I change the subject. 'The baths are huge. We can spend as long as we like in them. We were given coffee at church and I went to my first antenatal clinic.'

'You seem to be enjoying yourself at this home,' my mother snaps. 'That's not why we sent you there. Don't they discipline the girls?'

'We can't be late for meals and we have to let Mrs Clements know if we go out in the afternoon.'

'Which is one thing you won't be doing. I'll have to ring the home about that. It's tinned peaches for desert. Fetch the dishes, Jane.'

As we eat our peaches and evaporated milk, a stiff stillness settles on the room. I decide to ask for some pocket money, although the phrase seems ludicrous in the circumstances. 'Dad,' I start, since pocket money has always been from him, 'Could I have a couple of weeks' pocket money?'

'Whatever for?'

'I need to buy wool to knit some baby clothes.'

His upper lip tightens as if he's been eating lemons. 'Have you any idea how much this home is costing me?'

'I still need some spending money. They don't provide anything for the baby, not even the nappies. My maternity grant hasn't come through yet.'

'You'd better ask its father. I can't afford luxuries.'

I think of Tina. 'I'm sure some of the other girls aren't paying fees.'

'Maybe you can do something useful while you are there,' snaps my mother, 'and find out.'

I can't say I enjoyed those visits home. The following Sunday was Easter Day and my diary tells me I didn't go home as we had a sort of Easter party at the home. At church that morning, a baby girl who'd left the home a while ago was christened. I didn't like to ask if she was with her birth mother or whether she had been adopted.

Thirteen

One morning, as we gather for morning prayers, the whisper is that Sylvia went in during the night.

'I heard the ambulance,' insists Tina. 'I was up feeding.'

'But she isn't due for a week.' That's midwife Debbie.

I listen, not knowing anything of the procedure of actually having a baby.

Mrs Clements walks in and the chattering stops instantly. 'Good morning.'

Mrs Clements might not behave like a strict warden to a group of wayward women but we react to her as if we are rescued souls who are not yet forgiven. 'Good morning, Mrs Clements,' we chorus.

After prayers she says, 'I have some news. Sylvia had her baby during the night. A little girl. Seven pounds six ounces.'

Chattering breaks out.

'She wanted a girl.'

'Hope she's OK.'

'When can we visit?'

'I'll take her that matinee jacket I knitted. It'll suit a girl.'

Mrs Clements holds up her hand. 'No one today but two of you can go tomorrow. Decide which two and come and see me. Now I've got a letter for Tina.'

Monday brings a change of chores. This week, I'm on bathrooms, cleaning the huge, white baths, three of them, scrubbing the lavatories and polishing the basins and the taps. It's lonelier than the stairs, as the stairs are in the centre of the house and I can listen to the others, the banter as we go about our tasks, the crying for milk from the babies as the ten o'clock feed approaches. But the bathroom is a vast, chilly room at the back of the house, clearly added on when it became a home. I'm away from everyone else occupied with their work. Baths are allowed after lunch and between tea and supper, not in the morning or the evening.

I'm walking between the baths, when I hear someone crying. The sound is coming from the other side of one of the partition curtains. I hook a finger round the edge. It's Tina. She's holding a letter with typing on it. A long, brown envelope is on the floor.

'Problems?' I ask as gently as I can.

Tina sniffs. 'I've had me letter.'

'What about?'

'From me social worker. She's given me my date.'

'What date?'

Tina lifts her head and stares at me is if I'm a cretin.

'The date I take her to the office. The date she's going.'

The date she's going. This is what it's all about. The waiting for the day when the brown envelope arrives, giving the execution date, the day when the baby must be given away.

I risk putting an arm round her shoulder. 'What happens?'

Tina wriggles away to wipe her nose on a piece of toilet paper. Her voice shakes. 'Your social worker comes to collect you and the baby with its box.'

'Box?'

'You put the clothes and nappies in a cardboard box. You get one from the kitchen. Those large ones that have boxes of cornflakes in. You cover it with pretty paper if you like, you know, blue for a boy, pink for a girl.'

I nod, thinking *I won't have to do that. I'll be keeping my baby.*

'You take the baby with all its stuff up the office. You give the baby and the box to your social worker.'

She pauses.

'And then?'

'She takes the baby and the box from you.'

'What then?'

'You go home.'

I try to see this sorry episode in my head but there's a bit missing, the most important bit. 'What happens to the baby?'

'The social worker gives it over to the people what are adopting it.'

'Why, where are they?'

Tina gives me a pitying look. 'In the next room, aren't they? Waiting.'

'You don't see them?'

'No.'

I feel cold. 'Not ever?'

'What good would that do? You're never going to see your baby again are you? You clear about all that, then?'

'I don't have to be,' I say more confidently than I feel. 'I've got Nick, haven't I?'

'Where is he then?'

Tina has a point. That evening, I nip out to ring Nick. It's a quarter past six so I just have time before the supper bell rings. He might still be at work… he picks up.

'It's me,' I say, as if I'm a simpleton. 'How are you?' A voice in my head tells me that's his line, not mine. I wait.

'Fine Jane.'

There's a pause.

I try, 'I'm at the home. It's nice.'

Another wait.

I take a deep breath to steady me. 'I could do with a bit of money. You see I don't get maternity allowance as I didn't work and my grant…'

'I get the picture.'

'Well?'

'I'll pop over and see you.'

For some reason his use of the phrase pop over makes me livid. 'If we were married you wouldn't have to pop over, would you?'

'It's not going to happen quickly. You'll have to be patient.'

That does it. I let go. 'Patient?' I shout at him down the line. 'What the hell are you doing, Nick? Lazing around when you should be looking after me and your baby. Your baby, Nick, no one else's. Except mine of course.'

'Forget about the money, Jane. I'm done.' He hangs up on me.

◆ ◆ ◆

Next morning, Rachel still hasn't gone into labour yet and is anxious. She's received a letter from her father threatening to come down to London and see what the hell is going on.

In the lounge, I sip my hot chocolate, waiting for Tina to finish feeding.

She looks tired and tells me she was up twice in the night. With her usual resignation to life's problems she says, 'S'pect her routine is upset what with coming out of hospital.'

'I'll miss you.' I wait a minute and say, 'I hate asking you when you're upset…'

She sniffs and rubs her nose with her sleeve. 'I'm all right. Not much point in fussing. I'll be home soon. What's up?'

'Dad says the home is costing him a fortune and won't give me any more pocket money.'

'Pocket money? You're not at school any more. You're having a kid, aren't you?'

I nod.

'Get down the assistance office. Get them to pay. You'll have some left over, not millions but enough for soap and stuff and a bit for extras.'

I admit I don't know where the office is.

Tina looks at me as if I were loony. 'I thought you were bright.'

'They don't teach that kind of thing at grammar school.'

Tina walks out of the room leaving me sitting on the sofa feeling like the baby I'm expecting. Within a minute or two she returns with a telephone directory. 'You go to your local branch. Where d'you live?'

'Streatham, SW16.' Strictly speaking, our house is in Balham and according to my mother we live in Clapham

Park but I'm fairly sure our area is Streatham for this purpose.

She scans a list of local London offices of the National Assistance Board. 'Your branch is in Brixton. Ring them up and make an appointment. Ask Mrs Clements. She'll help you. It's what she's here for.'

I hug her. Then I say, 'What about your fella? Isn't he helping you?'

'Had to go and get myself knocked up by a married bloke, didn't I? Couldn't even find my own. Had to pinch someone else's.'

'What does his wife think of it all?

'Don't ask me. Never met her. Don't suppose I ever will. Come to think of it, I don't suppose she knows I even exist.' She lets out one of her high, childish laughs which seems totally incongruous with her story.

I'm fascinated by a world so unlike mine. 'Didn't the board want him to pay something?'

'Not much use if they did. I'm not telling anyone who he is. Even my old man doesn't know. I'll tell you something else. My bloke doesn't even know he's a father. Don't want him interfering.'

I'm astounded. Tina's the clever one.

'You don't want to involve your fella in this,' she continues. 'Keep him out of it. Once you take money from him you've lost your independence. If you take so much as a fiver from your fella, he can go to court and stop the adoption. It isn't worth it.'

And marvelling at how little I know of this world of fellas and illegitimate babies, I thank Tina for putting me straight. Suddenly it strikes me how young she looks to have such a reasoned attitude towards her dilemmas. 'How old are you, Tina?' The question is out before I have a chance to think of the consequences.

'I'm fifteen and don't you go saying I've no business having a fella at that age because it was him who got me. He was the one who should've known what he was getting me into.' And with that, she runs out of the room.

Fifteen. As far as I was aware, there had been no call for the father of her child to be accused of rape. Was it that Tina didn't count because she was from a poor home? Was she regarded as not worthy of the law's protection? But what good would it have done to drag her and her family through a court, to expose them all to the ridicule of others?

It wasn't long before I lost the pleasure of having a morning chat with Tina. One afternoon when I came down from my rest, I learnt her social worker had collected her and her baby. I never saw her again.

However hard I search my memory now, I have no idea how much money I received from the National Assistance Board. Somehow, I gleaned that the amount requested by the home was lower for a girl on Assistance then if she were a private resident, but I have no idea where that information came from. It's odd, the things a memory forgets. But I do remember that I wanted to do this on my own. It was time I started to grow up and take decisions for myself.

I knock on Mrs Clements' door and her calm voice tells me to 'Come in'. Quickly I confess that my father is complaining about the cost of the home, I don't want to ask Nick for money and I'd like to apply to the National Assistance Board.

She gives me a shrewd glance. 'You can phone from here. Sit down.'

Sitting at her desk, I telephone the National Assistance Board. Sounding more assured than I am, I explain I'm ringing to ask about help with paying for my maternity home.

A voice says, 'Just a moment please,' as if this is a common place request.

I am given a date for an interview for next week.

Although I'm not sure whether I will qualify for the benefit, I think my parents will be pleased to learn that my father might no longer have to pay for my exile.

I ring home.

'You're doing what?' my mother screeches.

'I've told you. I'm trying to get help with the money for the home. Not everyone pays fees. I don't get maternity allowance as I haven't any stamps and, anyway, I need some cash.' I add, 'I do have to wash and clean my teeth.'

Her verdict is harsh. 'You're begging.'

I become impatient. What does she want, for heaven's sake? 'I'm entitled to this, Mum. I just have to have an interview and explain.'

'Explain what exactly?'

'Not sure. But I'll do it. You'll see.'

There's a pause while she searches for a reason why what I'm doing is wrong. Then, 'Where is this office?'

'Off Brixton High Road. My appointment is for next week. Thursday morning. I'll get over there by bus.'

'You'll do no such thing. Suppose you are seen? Your father will take you in the car.'

Before I can hang up, she asks, 'What about this Sunday.'

'Let's skip it, Mum. Let's wait until we have the answer about the money.'

A week later, I stand on the pavement outside the home waiting. It's not long before I see my father park the car in a side street and beckon me to cross over to him. The journey to Brixton High Street passes in silence. The building is on a corner with the High Road.

'It'd be better if I go in alone,' I mutter.

'Whatever you say.' Terse voice, mouth grim set.

I'm making him feel a failure, a poor excuse for a father, which is not in my plan. My plan? I have no game plan, only to succeed with this move. Surely once my parents have no reason to resent the money they have to pay, things will improve.

A plain door with a dingy brass plate tells me I'm entering the premises of The National Assistance Board Local (South London) Branch. It opens onto a narrow dark corridor leading to a flight of stone steps. I wrinkle my nose against the burnt tinge to the air inside. Stale tobacco. It's almost too dark to see the edges of the steps. Above me sways a dead light bulb.

At the top of the steps is a second door with a handwritten notice pinned to it telling me to KNOCK AND ENTER.

I find a table with a typewriter on it, an empty chair and yet another door, this time open. Through it sits a woman wearing glasses and a smile specially created for wayward girls.

'Come in, dear,' spoken just as the wolf might have spoken to Little Red Riding Hood. 'What can we do for you?' Better.

I explain about the home and the fact that the fees for private girls is higher than those who have benefit and about my father having a mortgage since we moved to London.

The woman flicks through some papers. 'When's your baby due? We can only help with the last six weeks before the birth.'

Quickly I count. 'I'm just about that now.' Then, thinking this isn't going as smoothly as I hoped, I elaborate with a white lie. 'I'm still working for my A levels. If the baby comes on time I can probably take them and go to university next October.'

She doesn't believe me.

Time for a bigger lie. 'I've got a place.'

An amazed look. 'We don't usually get girls like you in here. Where is the father of the baby? I assume you know who the father is. We don't always get that either.'

'I know who the father is. I've only slept with one boyfriend.'

'Bit late for scrupulous morals.'

My skin flushes. I try to sound respectable. 'My father brought me here.'

If that's proof of my good intentions, the woman ignores it. 'Are you in touch with the father?'

'My father has forbidden me to see him.'

'Hmm.' She flicks more papers, suddenly looking up, sharply, accusingly. 'But you do?'

'No.' Not a lie.

'Can you get in touch with him?'

'Why?'

'Perhaps we can ask him to contribute in some way?'

Which makes me rush in. I'm sure Nick won't support me. He said so, didn't he? Although I still can't face the idea of giving my baby away, I'm beginning to accept that my future isn't bound up with Nick. Baby or no baby.

'I don't want money from the father. He wants the baby. If you must know, he's a bit soppy about it all. If he gives me money, he might try to stop the adoption.' I'm breathless by then, sounding appropriately young and schoolgirlish as if university rather than motherhood was the next natural step.

More flicking, more looking up and down. She closes the file. 'I'm going to recommend you for benefit.'

I send a silent prayer of thanks for Tina. The woman is still talking.

'You'll get the fees paid and three pounds ten shillings for spending money. You collect that directly from the home.' She pauses. 'The payment will be back dated so you'll get a windfall to spend on nappies.' She smiles.

I begin to tremble. For the first time since all this sad story has begun, I'm thankful. I have achieved something on my own, something which will help, not only me, but my parents as well. I have good news to bring to my mother. Who isn't so easily comforted. When I am able to ring to tell her I'd had a letter from the Board and my application had been accepted, her response is, 'I never thought my daughter would have her first baby on national assistance.'

Fourteen

Time at the home is marked by routine: breakfast, prayers, chores, coffee, knitting, lunch, afternoon walks or trips into Wimbledon, tea, listening to the radio, supper and early nights.

The passing weeks are also marked by departures and arrivals.

Sylvia's replacement in the ante-natal bedroom is Maggie, a red-haired young woman with an efficient manner about her. Maggie has her future planned out. 'I'm having this baby adopted. I'm with David now. He's supported me through all this, so I'm giving him what he wants. Once I'm out of here, I'm marrying him. The registry office is all booked.'

I wonder how Maggie can be quite so sure of everything. Suppose she changes her mind once she is holding her baby. Will David support her then?

One afternoon, I go into town with Maggie and, after I get back, Mrs Clements calls me into her room.

'I saw you leave with Maggie this afternoon.'

'Yes, Maggie was buying some new shoes for after the baby…' I couldn't finish my sentence.

'I don't want you to get too friendly with Maggie. Don't get too involved with her. I don't want her to influence you.'

I left, puzzled. How could Maggie possibly influence me? We couldn't be in such different situations. For one thing, I have no one offering to marry me, with or without my baby.

Still, I keep a distance between us. I don't want to hurt her feelings. Even though Tina has gone, leaving an empty space, I don't want to get close to a newcomer.

It's the first Sunday in May. My visit home is going smoothly if tensely, as we sit eating roast lamb.

Until my mother announces, 'At least this home isn't eating up your father's salary anymore.' She dips her head, concentrating on forking up some spring greens. 'But we're still hoping to have you home early.' She is making this sound as if it's good news which, I've learnt, means is where I need to take notice. 'You know,' she adds, 'Afterwards.'

She still can't say it. Even with me safely locked away from the doctor, the neighbours, from London itself, she can't bring herself to say the word birth. But that isn't the bit which amazes me. The bit which astounds me is that mum is willing to have us home afterwards. Me and my baby.

I smile gently, not triumphantly. I've learnt that happiness is never the mood of the moment, whatever might be said. 'That'll be something to look forward to, won't it, Mum? You and me and the baby.' I must be cracked.

Lots of blinking and rolling of eyes, staring all the time at the mint sauce. Finally, the naked truth. 'Don't be ridiculous, Jane. You know perfectly well there's no question of a baby here. How can we hide a baby from the neighbours even for a couple of weeks?'

She's lost me. 'A couple of weeks?'

'Your father is hoping to hurry things up.'

'What things?'

'You know perfectly well, Jane. Your father will see Mrs Bird and arrange for the adoption papers to be drawn up. Things can happen quickly. Then you can look forward to coming home. On your own.'

My baby kicks me. I put a hand on my bump and wince.

For just a second my mother looks worried. 'What's the matter? Are you all right?'

I put the flat of my hand against my domed abdomen. A hard knob of cartilage sticks out of my belly. A hand maybe, or a heel or an elbow. My baby. I let myself smile my happiness. 'I'm fine. So is my baby. Mum, there's not going to be an adoption. I'm not arguing with you, or shouting or listening to you shouting at me. If you won't help me, I'll have to make Nick help me.'

Not good enough. Instantly her expression turns bitter. 'Have you seen him? Has he been over to the home? Because if he's ignored the solicitor's letter…'

Solicitor? My heart thumps. 'What letter?'

'Your father's instructed our solicitor to write to Nick forbidding him to see you.'

'He's done what?'

My father gives a short cough, a clearing of his throat. 'I asked Chapels to confirm the position. That's what solicitors are for.'

'What exactly did this letter say?'

My father finishes his mouthful and stands up. 'You can read it yourself. I kept a copy, of course.' He leaves the room and I listen to him going upstairs.

After a minute or so he comes back with one of those manila files he borrows from the office. I'm officially filed away, neatly categorised. No doubt I'll be brought forward when the time is right. I take the piece of paper he holds out to me.

Solicitors' headed notepaper. Black type. Cold words.

Dear Sir,

NOTICE OF PROPOSED ORDER UNDER SECTION …

I have been instructed by my client Mr… to inform you that his daughter Jane has been accepted at the institution known as St Mary's Home for Mothers and Babies. I have been instructed not to divulge the address of the establishment.

My client's daughter Jane has complied with her father's request not to contact you and has agreed that the child be put under supervision of the Court of Adoption at the appropriate time.

My client wishes you to know that you are to desist from contact with his daughter either in person or by letter or telephone. If you do not comply with this request, it will be enforced by an order under Section…

Yours faithfully, A. Crawshore

On behalf of Chapels, Commissioner for Oaths.

No wonder Nick hasn't been in touch. This is what he meant when he said he was done. Done with me, most definitely. Who would want to see the woman who agrees to have her child given away to the best bidder? What must he be imagining, what must he think of me?

I glare at my father. I hate him. 'You had no right to tell such a hideous lie.' I'm trembling but I have no doubt. My father's act of total disloyalty and my mother's connivance with him settle my feelings for them in stone.

My father coughs again. 'We are only doing what is right for you, Jane.'

I stand up. 'I'd like to go home now. The home which is my home.'

My mother begins to work her face, press her lips together, blinking faster than ever. 'Jane, you must believe…' she begins.

'Believe? I believe nothing. I'll leave that to you. I know one thing though. This baby will not go away. Soon he'll be here in person. And I intend to keep him with me and do whatever I can to look after him. Now I want to go back to the home and stay there. I won't be making any visits back here, no more cosy Sunday lunches.'

It's then that my mother stands up, takes a quick step towards me and hits me. Twice. Smartly on the right cheek, harder on the left.

Just for a second, I lose my balance and my body tips towards the table's edge, but I reach for the chair back and straighten up. I can feel each finger mark as it warms into a pattern on my skin. Tears I will not allow. I do not scream at her or even shout. I tell myself not to care enough to say a single word. I don't look at her, not meet her eye with mine, nor give her another moment of satisfaction.

I march out of the room, out of the house and turn into the road.

I take the northern line from Balham, changing at Embankment for the district and again at Earls Court for the Wimbledon train. I have no money for the bus so walk up the hill to the village and then along The Ridgeway to number fifty-four.

I am exhausted.

Mrs Clements opens the door to me and says straightaway, 'Do you want to have a few minutes in my room?'

I cry then, my shoulders shaking and my chest heaving. My baby lies still, listening to my heart.

Mrs Clements puts her arm around me and agrees I can refuse to go home if that's what I really want. She says, 'I think it will be better for you to stay here until the baby arrives. Afterwards, we'll think again.'

This week I'm on kitchens. I peel potatoes, chop cabbage and onions for the shepherd's pie with a letter from my mother unopened. I read it while drinking coffee.

Dear Jane,

I don't know what to say to you after your dreadful behaviour to us on your visit home. You upset me for the whole of the week. I'm sure some of the other girls are quite pleasant but this is your home and we expect to see you here.

You know all I want is for you to be happy in the right kind of way. You could get married to Nick tomorrow but how? He hasn't a penny and, even living with his mother, how will you manage?

You need to have time to think. Since there are so many things to discuss, your father and I will pick you up after church on Sunday 9th. We're looking forward to having the chance to talk things over.

Your loving Mother.

I found that letter, tucked inside the back cover of my diary. Was it the only letter of hers I kept? That wouldn't surprise me as, instead of our relationship improving with me out of the way, it deteriorated.

I don't remember my reaction. Despair, I imagine. But might I have been relieved that my parents were still there? They were still the only visible support I had. Apart from the girls at the home. Was that the moment when I began to think that adoption might be my choice? If the other girls could do it, why couldn't I? It was years later that I learnt there was a statutory time before which babies could not be given up for adoption. That was why the mothers had to stay in the home for six weeks after the birth. Whatever they might want, they had to wait for six weeks before they could leave the home without their baby. They had six weeks to learn to love him or her and then they were forced to give their child away. That did seem cruel.

It's Saturday. A hot day. By half past ten the sun is lighting up the chintz covers on the lounge chairs, inviting us to move outside to the garden, to breathe in clear air rather than the warm, milky fug rising from the coffee trolley.

I'm helping myself to a cup of hot chocolate when Mrs Clements puts her head round the door. 'There you are, Jane. You've got a visitor. Maybe she'd like a coffee.'

'Hope you do frothy,' says a voice and I almost drop the jug of hot milk.

'Rita. How the... what are you doing here?'

She's dressed in the latest trend, a white polo neck jumper made of some thin yarn which clings to her body and a skirt of blue denim about as wide as a curtain pelmet. Her black hair is still cut short and sharp, her eyes finely outlined. She's thinner than I remember.

I wonder now what Mrs Clements thought of her, but she must have approved of something or Rita would not have been allowed to cross the threshold.

'What's happened to the mod look?' I want to know.

'Gave all that up. It wasn't our fault but we got as much trouble from the police as the rockers so I changed tack.'

I grin. 'Still arranging life to suit yourself. Bunking off school?'

'Where's that coffee? Took me hours on the bus.'

We sit together on the sofa to exchange news. I learn that A levels are about to begin, and I imagine myself back at school with nothing more than revision to worry about. For all her change of costume, Rita seems much the same as she had been six months ago whereas I know I have changed although still have a great deal of growing up to do over the next few weeks.

With the lounge filling up with the others in from their chores, I became shy. My bump has grown, and we are surrounded by other girls all pregnant and all very different from Rita.

She must sense it too for she jumps up. 'Let's go.'

'Where?'

'They let you out, don't they?'

'In the afternoons.'

'Ask the old dear who let me in. She seems OK.'

Mrs C agrees on the condition I am not late for lunch. She smiles at me as if she's glad I have a friend. I enjoy walking down the hill to the shops with someone normal, not a girl who has disgraced herself and society.

'Just imagine,' says Rita, 'if the people on this hill knew there was a house of ill repute so close.'

Her laughter makes me defensive. 'The people at church don't mind.'

'Forgive you, do they?'

I mimic the woman who was kind to me, 'It's no use crying over spilt milk,' but immediately feel rotten about it. The woman was kinder to me than my own mother and she had no need to be.

'Probably tell their daughters to look at you lot and mind they don't end up like you. Made a decision, have you?'

'What about?'

'I saw Les the other day and he said Nick and you had split.'

A huge stone of black granite turns over in my chest and tears sit on my eyeballs, stinging. How could Nick talk to Les about me, about us, without even writing to me? Struggling to keep control I manage, 'Les must have it wrong,' while *You know she's right* spins round my head, strangling my dreams, my plans for my baby. 'I haven't heard from Nick recently.'

'You'll have the baby adopted then?'

What does Rita know about adoption?

I shrug. 'I haven't a clue.' I don't want to talk to Rita about my baby, I don't want ideas getting back to Nick. 'I need to buy some wool,' I say. 'I'll do that while you're with me.'

I'm not wearing a coat. Dressed only in a summer smock I look quite the young mum-to-be.

In the wool shop I wait patiently, two ounces of blue baby wool in my hand. The elderly owner ignores me. I cough politely, hold out my money. Money as good as anyone else's. She looks the other way. Eventually, I walk behind the counter. 'I'd like this please.'

She gives me a look of rude contempt. She's thinking, another unmarried mum. Another girl who's no better than she should be. But she takes my money.

'Why didn't you say?' demands Rita when we are out of the shop.

'Say what?'

'The way that woman treated you. As if you were dirt.'

'She thinks I am.' I don't care about the wistful note in my voice.

We walk in silence for a few minutes, along the High Road, the part where the big stores are, the department store and Woolworth's. In the shadow of that famous store with its red lettering spelt high above the door, Rita stops. 'Follow me,' she tells me.

I do, through the doors, their frames painted bright red, into the shop where everything once cost sixpence. She leads me straight to the jewellery counter, to the displays of fake emeralds, gleaming a poisonous green, to the sapphires a

172

deep, dubious blue, the diamonds, glittering hard and to the wedding rings, gold which would peel off in the hot washing up water.

'Choose one,' she orders.

'Why?'

Rita gives a great sigh. 'If you wear a ring no one will know, will they? You'll be married so it'll be OK.'

The rings are one shilling and sixpence. I pick up one but put it down again. Another lie. Another fraud. 'It's all wrong. Choosing a wedding ring should be one of the most romantic times in my life. Why am I buying my own ring?'

'Because you're up the Swanee with no fella. You have a point though. No one should buy their own wedding ring. My treat.' She pulls out her purse.

I choose a band of gold set in two bands of silver. Pretty enough. For one and sixpence. It fits. It does the job.

Rita grins. 'That's settled then. Now will my married friend walk with me to the tube station? I've got to get ready for a night on the Island.' And we link arms.

I owe Rita.

Fifteen

As the next Sunday approaches, I try to forget my apprehension over my mother's threat to collect me. I fill my hours with housework, knitting and sleeping. Thursday is wet and, to our delight, Mrs Clements lends us her tape player and Georgie feeds in her new tapes. We sit and tap our feet to Little Things, but when the beat of Concrete and Clay fills the room, we are up on our feet and moving ourselves about, those who still await the arrival of their babies cradling their bumps with clasped hands, as if their baby might fall to the floor any minute.

Rolling Stones rendering of The Last Time divides us into those who sit down and those who keep going, doing the hippy-hippy shake until they are breathless. Georgie dances in a jerky way that I've never seen before. At one point, Rachel flops into a chair saying, 'I know I've got to watch my blood pressure, but if this doesn't bring the baby on I don't know what will.' Someone calls out, 'a dose of castor oil!'

I dance with them all, enjoying the sense of being together, being part of a gang, wondering if my movements are waking the baby up or rocking it to sleep. Finally, we sit to listen to Marianne Faithfull implore her lover to Come and Stay with Me. If only.

After that dancing, I need a bath, an activity which is a mixture between privacy and communal living. Each bath is surrounded by plastic curtains but even with them drawn, it's impossible not to be aware that, sometimes, another mum-to-be is bathing in the next cubicle.

The curtains around the bath I have chosen are not completely tight, so I can just see between the edges of the thin, plastic sheet, blue with a print of dolphins playing in the waves.

I turn both taps full on, making it clear I'm not prying but intent on my own bath but, as I take off my dressing gown, I peep. I can't help it. The person in the next cubicle is Debbie, her very grown-up body swollen huge with her baby. Ignoring the water pounding into my bath, I stare at this female form, naked, distended in the way mine would become; the skin tightly stretched with blue veins running across the lower half of her bump like streams running down the side of a mountain. As she turns sideways on to me, I see her belly button sticking out, as if her baby is pushing from inside, calling, This is me. I'm here, ready to meet you.

I look down at my own small, hard hump; my still unblemished skin and my fuller, but not enormous, breasts. I move my hands over my body, feeling free to explore and encourage. I experience the stirrings of something miraculous and a wonderful acceptance of what was happening to me. However, as I step into the deep, hot bath, I still can't see how I will welcome my child into the world when the only family I have is determined to be hostile.

The next day, after the letters are handed out, Rachel opens hers, reads it and rushes out of the room. Mrs

Clements follows and we hear the click of the office door. Rachel is being allowed to make a phone call.

By mid-morning drinks time, the expectant mums know what it's all about. Rachel has received a letter from her father, asking what the hell is going on. He can't get any sense from his sister (Rachel's helpful aunt) and he's coming down to London to see Rachel herself. The only saving grace for Rachel is that her phone call established he was too busy and wouldn't be able to travel for a couple of weeks but by that time she had better be ready with a plausible story about all this secrecy.

According to Rachel, there's only one answer. She'll have to drink a bottle of castor oil that night, the baby's delivery will be brought on and she'll be out of hospital in time to face her father.

I remember the teaspoonsful of gloopy, thick cod liver oil I took as a child and shudder. Will it work? Will Rachel triumph in her effort to deceive her father? I vow to stay awake all night waiting for the sound of the ambulance.

Woken by Rachel's moaning, as she leaves our room and climbs the stairs to Sue's room, I lie, listening, long enough to be frightened to death by the noise coming from upstairs. Rachel's screams are terrible. I cannot imagine the pain she must be going through. However, I'm not so concerned that I manage to stay awake. When I do wake, light's coming in round the curtains and I learn at breakfast that Rachel's in hospital.

While we're eating lunch, Mrs Clements looks in to say that Rachel has a seven pound boy. Are her eyes twinkling because she knows what Rachel had got up to?

The story ends happily. Once back from hospital, Rachel meets her father to return to the home beaming. 'He said he couldn't understand why the dickens I'd made such a thing about wanting a bit of privacy.'

'What did you tell him?' we chorused.

'Nothing.'

So, one grandfather never knew he had a grandchild. How many men exist in the same state of ignorance? Or women for that matter? Mothers who were never told they had become grandmothers because the new mum was too scared of the consequences? How I wished my mother could find a little bit of love for her future grandchild, but it seemed it was never to be.

Sunday morning and we return from church to find the door being opened to us, not by Mrs Clements who has a day off, but a woman who is a stranger to me. Unlike Mrs Clements, she is tall and massive, like a boulder plonked in the hall. Unlike Mrs Clements, she is wearing a uniform, a dark navy dress with white collar and cuffs and leather belt.

'Which one is Jane?' she demands.

I own up. What have I done?

'Your mother rang. They'll be here in twenty minutes.'

I take a deep breath. 'I'm not going home today. Mrs Clements said…'

She glares. 'Don't be ridiculous. Your parents are coming for you and you'll do as you're told.'

I try again. 'You don't understand. Mrs Clements said…'

'Mrs Clements is not here and I am. Get your coat. It might be warm weather, but we don't want all the neighbours staring at you, do we?'

In spite of everyone's encouragement to stick myself on the sofa and refuse to budge, I give in. Battling with this woman, maybe physically as well as mentally, is out of the question. My bump is bulging now, and I don't have the energy.

I sit in the lounge and wait for the bell to ring.

I'm hardly in the car before my mother starts. 'I can't believe you're still going to church in your state.'

I keep quiet.

My mother won't let go. 'I mean, what on earth must people think? Especially the younger ones. How do their mothers explain?'

Silence.

'I hope you're not still going out locally.'

'Of course I am. I have to buy toothpaste, soap, washing powder. And when I can afford it, nappies and wool.'

My father sighs and shifts gear so the car can pick up speed.

Then I make a mistake. 'Actually, Rita came to see me this week. We went into town... She's...'

'I don't want to hear about that common girl. What was the matron thinking of? Doesn't she have any control?'

'Not over us like that. We are allowed out as long as our jobs are done. We just have to be back...'

'I don't care when you have to be back. You shouldn't be out at all. The sooner this is all over the better. When we get home, one or two things are going to be settled for good.'

I've had enough. I can either yell back or burst into tears. Neither will get me anywhere. The car is sitting at lights. I open the door and put a foot outside. I move towards the gap, but the lights change and suddenly the ground is speeding fast and then faster. 'Slow down Dad,' I call. 'I'm getting out. Now.'

The car swerves to a stop. Another vehicle hoots at us.

My father turns around in his seat. 'Don't be a fool. We can't leave you stranded here.' He turns back to my mother. 'Leave her be. After we've eaten, we'll try to talk sensibly.'

My mother huffs.

My father puts the car in gear.

I pull the door shut and sit, watching the real world passing me by. I don't bother to wipe the tears from my face as I'd rather believe they're not there. I've failed.

'Why,' says my mother, once we are eating our beef, 'are you wearing that ring?'

'So people will talk to me.'

'Which people?'

'In the shops. At the clinic. Where they insist on calling us all Mrs so we are not an embarrassment.'

'Now you know then,' says my mother.

'What?'

'What a disgrace you are. How shameful you are. How difficult you have made things for other people. For all the doctors who have to attend to you. I can't think what will happen when it finally happens. How dreadful it will be. Especially for me.'

Thus starts the whole diatribe again. How dreadful my behaviour has been, how I deceived her with that useless lay-about, how she worries herself sick at night wondering what's going to happen to us all, how I've let her down.

'Your father has spoken to Mrs Bird about the adoption form.'

179

'Which form?'

'The one to be signed giving authority for the adoption.'

I feel sick. I begin, 'I don't think Nick will sign it…'

'Nick? Who cares what he thinks? The point is that even your father can't sign it. Even though you're still not twenty-one. If you'd been under sixteen we could have applied to a court but as it is…'

'Yes. As it is?'

Her nerve almost lets her down. She doesn't want to tell me. Doesn't want to admit that at last I have a choice. 'You have to sign it yourself. So think about it and what the consequences will be if you refuse.'

I don't cry or shout at her. I tell myself not to care enough. My mother's brand of comfort I can do without. I can't even think straight until my baby is here and I still hang on to the hope that, when that has happened, when Nick holds the child in his arms, he will do the right thing. How could he not? I vow, once I am safely back at 54 The Ridgeway, I'll never go home again.

I return to the home to hear that Debbie is in hospital. My world here is changing. No longer am I the new antenatal mum who doesn't know any of the mothers. My new friends are becoming mothers and my circle of friends includes babies. Ten days later, Debbie comes back with a boy; Georgie goes in and doesn't come back at all. The story is that her parents have flown in from the States and taken both mother and baby home. Mrs Clements won't confirm or deny so we agree a happy ending once in a while cheers us all.

New expectant mums arrive. There's already Julie and Maggie. Now we have Sandra, whose parents run a pub in the Wandsworth area and who is engaged to the father of her baby. She wears a diamond ring but none of us are envious. She has an air of resignation about her which does not sing of absolute bliss. Laura arrives with such a large suitcase of clothes we wonder what they are all for but daren't ask. For a week we have an empty bed in the ante-natal room, until Violet arrives, a diminutive, pretty girl with black skin and almost navy blue curly hair. I can't wait to see her baby. There's one advantage of this policy of my mother's to keep me out of sight for longer than normal. I'll see more girls than I would otherwise, more of the world of adoption.

May continues to be warm. I live in my blue and white cotton smock dress, one from last summer.

One morning, I sit in a blur of happiness mixed with apprehension while Mrs Clements distributes more post. In my hand I hold a letter from Nick. My name, the address, all written with his brown ink in sloping copper-plate.

I can hardly believe it. After all this time. I haven't bothered counting the days since I last saw him, only the days forward to when my baby is expected and it's not many.

Deciding that vacuuming the stairs can wait for ten minutes, I leave the room and go to my bed. I have to know. Am I destined to go on with Nick, for the two of us to keep our baby, to make a family, to hope our love will be enough to bring up a baby? Or will Nick's letter tell me he's opted out, abandoned me to become a big man in the big world? Will the letter leave me with the ultimate opt-out clause, the one chance I have, in my mother's words, to get this business over with? And the thing which frightens me most is that I no longer know what I want.

I have no idea whether I want to keep my baby or give it up. So, like it or not, I'm totally dependent on what Nick says in his letter.

My fingers shake. At last his words. 'I'd like to talk. Can I come over? Would that be OK? As soon as possible. Don't tell your parents.' He hasn't signed off with all his love, just Nick.

How easily I am carried away with hope. I tell Mrs Clements Nick wants to see me and she agrees to him coming here. I ring him but have to make do with speaking to Ma. His absence brings back all my doubt again and I wonder if I am making a fool of myself.

I say to Ma, 'Can he come over next Monday evening? About seven?'

All she says is, 'He'll be there.'

Sixteen

I receive a letter from my mother. She writes:

Dear Jane,

You know all I want is for you to be happy in the right kind of way. You could get married to Nick tomorrow but how? He hasn't a penny and, even living with his mother, how will you manage?

Mrs Clements tells me you are unhappy. Does she imagine we are enjoying life? She also told me that Nick is to visit you at the home. I don't understand. You haven't told me he has been in touch. How can we resolve matters if you persist in deceiving me?

Try not to worry. Perhaps everything will turn out all right. Perhaps we will have a miracle...

I throw the letter down. Honestly. A miracle! Even I don't expect that from Nick. Where does she think she is? On planet heaven?

Once more I'm in Matron's sitting room. Monday is her day off and Sue is not as indulgent as her boss. 'You have half an hour,' she warns.

'An hour,' I plead. 'We have so much to talk about.'

She agrees but with the safeguard that she looks in on us now and again. Heavens what does she imagine? That we'll have rampant sex on Mrs Clements' rug?

'With me this size?' I say to Nick, laughing.

But he doesn't laugh back.

So my heart isn't leaping as I sit in an armchair and watch him. Watch him, rather than look at him. I need to be certain what he's planned for us and our baby. All my expectations are deserting me. The only way to describe him is shifty.

'So,' he says, after giving me a quick kiss on the cheek, 'what's it like in here?'

Pleased he is interested I describe the others to him, tell him about the chores we have to do.

All he can say is, 'I bet the food's lousy.'

'We have a proper cook. I've learnt how to make things I can do when we're married. Economical things mum doesn't do, like shepherd's pie.'

He finishes his coffee.

Mine has gone cold.

Nick hasn't said a word about getting married or me moving in with him and his mother. He hasn't told me anything at all about his job.

I watch him turn his empty mug round and round before taking the lead and questioning him. 'How much do you take home at the end of the week? Or are you paid monthly?'

'Not monthly, Jane. Definitely not monthly.'

'How much?' I sound impatient, but how can we plan, unless we talk about money for food and stuff like washing powder for the baby's nappies, if I don't know how much he earns? 'Nick, we have to plan ahead. How much do you earn?'

'Nothing. I earn nothing.'

I laugh, actually laugh, I'm that sure he's mucking about. 'Joke over. How much?' I produce something I've done earlier, a foolscap piece of paper divided into columns headed rent, bills, food and extras. Just as if I was on Blue Peter. But this is real life.

I show it to Nick. 'It's not all bad news. The column headed extras includes going to the cinema. If we have enough over at the end of the week.'

'We won't have.' He drinks quickly and slams down the mug on the table. 'There'll be nothing left over because I won't be earning anything. I gave the job up, Jane. I quit.' He glances out of the window. He can't look at me, can't face me. He's telling the truth.

I refuse to cry. Or to weaken. 'You can't. We, I mean me and the baby, we need you to help us. No one else will,' I add bitterly.

He gives me that soft, imploring look. 'Jane my love, you must understand. It was so, so...' he looks around the room as if searching for inspiration, 'limiting.'

Limiting! This is more than enough. 'What do you think this is?' I pat my swollen belly. 'This is limiting.'

He has the grace to look ashamed. 'Sorry.' He pauses as if he's thinking of something to make me feel better, something to encourage me. 'I hated it. I'd have died if I'd stayed.'

I'm not listening. 'When did you give the job up?'

He jingles money in his pocket. Money Pa gave him, I suppose. 'I stuck at it for a couple of months. I did try.'

'A couple of months? You mean to tell me that recently you haven't worked at all?'

'Sorry.'

'Don't you sorry me. What's sorry is that I'm expecting your child and we have to get a home together and buy clothes and food and milk powder and pay the rent and the bills and you can't even hang on to a job for more than two months?'

He remains silent.

'What happens now?' I don't care if I'm nagging him. 'What do I tell my parents? Or Mrs Bird if it comes to that?'

'Mrs Bird knows,' he says.

'What exactly does she know?' I pause, then add, 'And since when?'

'I told her. I had to, Jane. She was ringing me up with appointments to go and see flats. What could I do?'

'You told Mrs Bird before me?' I'm sad and angry at the same time. And then very cold. 'When were you going to tell me?'

He doesn't answer. Just looks at the floor and jingles the money in his pocket.

My voice drops to a whisper. But an urgent whisper. 'What do you suggest then?'

'Don't know, Jane. I just don't know.' Then he looks me in the eye as if he has nothing to hide, as if he was being honest with me. 'I do love you.'

I weaken. 'You're looking for something else, then? They gave you references.'

'Not quite.'

'What do you mean not quite? Either they did, or they didn't. Which?'

'Didn't. You see Jane,' he stands up and I have the dreadful foresight that a certain kind of end is imminent, 'They sacked me.'

I sit not saying anything, not even looking at him. At the father of my baby who is a no-hoper, a wastrel, a nothing.

He kneels before me, actually gets down on one knee as if he's begging. He certainly isn't proposing. The difference doesn't matter to me anymore because my insides are cold. There's no love there, not for him. My insides are full of baby. No room at the inn for its father. I listen to his words but they're not in my world any more, they're out there, in space, creating their own black hole.

'It doesn't matter because, you see Jane, I'm leaving London. I'm going to Hollywood. To make films.' He takes my hands in his. 'It'll be all right. You'll see. You hang on here and have the baby and I'll be back for you. For you both. Just as soon as I can.' He drops my hand and stands up.

I'm still watching. 'After you've made a couple of films, is that it?'

He laughs. 'I knew you'd understand, Jane. I'll be rich and you and the baby, we'll live in style. Just as you deserve.'

A swirl of revulsion churns in my stomach. My mother and father are waiting at home for me to take myself back to them without the stain in my abdomen while they also fear Nick is about to steal me from them. That they will be forced to visit their poor but respectable married daughter. Even their worst scenario is not going to come true. None of it will happen. Their version of the story is the correct

187

one. I've let myself be taken in by a skunk and I'm being dumped and left to become an unmarried mother with my illegitimate baby.

'Get out.' My voice is as cruel as my mother's. 'Just go.'

He tries to kiss me, but I shy away, pushing out with my hands against him. He falls backwards, stumbling, putting a hand against a chair. 'OK, OK, I'm going. Don't be angry with me, Jane.'

'I'm not.' I mean it. For I can see he can't help himself. He is weak and pathetic and no use to me or my baby. No longer does Nick have any part in us. From this moment on it is my baby.

'You will tell me when the baby comes, won't you, Jane?'

I look at him, wondering whether even he believes in himself. 'I thought you were going to be in the States?'

'I'll leave a number with the Dicky-Bird.'

I stay in the room as I hear him go downstairs.

After a few minutes the door opens and in comes Sue in her crisp blue dress.

'Everything settled?' she says.

Back in my bedroom, standing by my bed, I put my arms around my bump. Around my baby.

'What shall we do now?' I whisper. 'Now we are alone?'

At my next clinic appointment, I'm told my blood pressure is raised and I need a salt-free diet.

The nurse flicks through my records. 'You're at the Ridgeway?'

I nod.

'We'll write to the matron.'

She leaves, and the doctor arrives to feel around my bump. He asks me again when my baby is due.

'Beginning of June,' I tell him.

He reads my notes and frowns. 'It says here there's some doubts about your dates.'

'Maybe the middle.'

'It's still upside down but there's time.'

'Time for what?'

'The head isn't engaged. Don't miss next week's clinic. If necessary, we'll have to try to turn it. Let's put the expected date of delivery at 14 June, shall we? Then we'll all know where we are.'

Some hope!

Sylvia's baby is called Holly. Since she's been back at the home, Sylvia's been answering adverts for a mother's help, some of which offer a home to an unmarried woman with a child. She asks me to babysit Holly. 'I've got an interview next week.'

'Have you found a job as a mother's help?' I ask.

She grins. 'Actually, it's as a father's help. The man is coming up to London. We're meeting in the members' coffee room of the Royal Academy.' She almost giggles. 'Couldn't be more respectable.'

I hadn't expected an interview with a man. As if Sylvia has read my thoughts, she adds, 'He's a widower with three children. Lives near to Chelmsford.'

'Three children?'

'And he doesn't mind a baby. He must be a kind man.'

A kind man. It's one solution and probably not a bad one.

'So will you look after Holly for me?' she asks again.

'I'd love to.'

We agree I give the two o'clock feed so Sylvia can get to Piccadilly in plenty of time.

'I should be back easily by six,' she says. 'If I get the job, I'll need another sit while I buy a pram.'

Buy a pram. My heart tumbles. Will that ever be me buying a pram?

Sylvia mutters more to herself than me, 'I'd better decide what to wear. I think I'll get my hair cut.' And she goes out to the telephone box to phone the hairdresser.

In spite of keeping her baby, one mother is returning to everyday life. Normal life. If only I could see my future. I push the tea trolley back to the kitchen and then get back to my knitting. Whatever happens, my child will have a full wardrobe.

At night the babies sleep next to their mothers, each one in turn waking the whole room so that the mums spend the day walking round like zombies. They do not, of course, have to do chores. Their energy is all spent on their new charges.

During the day the infants are in their cots in the nursery, asleep, in a large bright room at the back of the house, next to Mrs Clements' private sitting room. Off one corner is a small kitchen, Sue's domain. She makes up the bottles, supervises the cleaning and sterilising of the equipment and hovers during feeds, making sure the new mums are caring for their babies. Is she, I wonder now, also making sure they do not love their babies too much, helping them towards the time when respectable society will split their offspring from them, like peeling a baby orange segment away from the full-size fruit?

I cradle Sylvia's baby in the crook of my left arm, leaning her gently back until I can look into her eyes, a vivid blue with a navy line around the irises and pupils as dark as ebony.

In my right hand I hold Holly's bottle, made of thick glass with a rubber teat. The milk is warm but not hot. I test it on the inside of my wrist as Sylvia showed me before she left.

'I know you haven't been in here yet,' she said, 'but Debbie will be feeding Sam if you need help.' She laughed. 'He's so huge and greedy.' She showed me the fridge where the bottles of made-up milk are kept and how to warm the milk in hot water. 'Shake it up. Undissolved powder can clog the teats.'

More to learn. 'I'll be fine.'

'If I have time, I'll look for a pram in that baby shop in the high street. That OK?'

'Fine. I'll keep an eye on her.' I took a deep breath. I had to ask. 'Are you sure? You don't have any doubts?'

'About keeping Holly? Positive.' She put an arm round me and hugged me. 'I know you'll reach the right decision, Jane. It's different for me.'

How did she know I had a decision to make? My official line was always 'I've got Nick'. But Sylvia was one of those people who knew intuitively when there was a problem, when someone was worrying. She'd make the perfect mother's help. 'How is it different for you?'

She pulled a long face. 'I'm old, nearly thirty. I won't get married now. Holly is the only baby I'll have. But you're young. You've got time. You'll marry and have another baby.'

The room is quiet, the warm silence broken only with soft sucking and low murmurs as mums whisper to their babies how much they love her or him and how he or she must finish their bottle to grow big and strong. To grow into a child they will never see.

Sitting among them, I feel grown-up, responsible. I am also afraid. I look at Holly and try to imagine myself with my baby. And can't. I can't see myself with Nick's baby at his mother's house, putting him to bed in that narrow room still with a single bed in it covered by that stained pink bedspread. I can't see us anywhere else, not in a flat, just the two of us and I certainly can't see me with my baby back at my parents' house. Which means I still can't imagine living with my baby at all. He remains a lump inside me, although he's growing every day, disturbing me, kicking me at night, sticking an elbow out as I drink my morning coffee.

Holly opens her mouth, nuzzling inwards towards my breast, rooting. As I have to believe my baby will root, seeking me out.

Now I slip the teat between Holly's gums and watch her lips close and suck. And make myself think again what Sylvia meant when she said, 'You'll have another baby.'

She meant not to bother keeping this one. I'm young. I've got the time to give up this baby inside me now and wait until another one comes along. When the time is right. When I'm married. What Sylvia was doing was advising me to have my baby adopted.

And I can't look at Holly any more but stare out of the window, keeping my back turned against the other mothers in the room for fear they will see my eyes. But I don't know why I am crying because if I can't imagine my baby, if I can't believe in it, why should it bother me to give it away?

Sylvia returns to the home in a triumphant flurry. 'I've got the job! I've got the job! It's all fixed.'

Of course, we clamour round her, clutching our cups of tea, begging for all the details.

'He was a kind man,' she begins...

'They all are to begin with,' some wit says.

'He was wearing a dark suit and shook my hand and called me Miss Stevenson. His children are called...'

We listen, admiring her enthusiasm for her future life with this man and his children, but envious of her happiness, wishing there's some magic answer to the inevitable climax to our stories.

The clock on the mantelpiece chimes six and Sylvia and the other mums leave for their babies' feeds.

I'm lucky enough to be a babysitter once again, while Sylvia is shopping. A pram stands in the hall, a painful reminder to us all of what we won't have. A week or so later, Sylvia and Holly leave in a taxi provided by Sylvia's new boss.

Reader, she will marry him.

Seventeen

It seems I am to be left alone to prepare for the arrival of my baby in peace. Nick has gone, from my life if not from the country, and my mother has clearly given up bothering or caring about me. I have my new friends with their babies and me with mine, jiggling and jolting around inside me. My bump is now big enough for me to balance a cup of tea on the top of it. I'm eating a tasteless salt free diet and sleeping deeply in the afternoon.

However, one morning I'm given the familiar blue envelope with my mother's sloping handwriting in royal blue ink.

Dear Jane,

Mrs Clements has written to ask us not to visit you. Something to do with high blood pressure and you needing rest. Your father and I are disappointed with her lack of support.

We are your parents after all. You give us no choice but to take further steps to make you take your situation seriously.

I know we aren't getting on at the moment but don't forget that after this is all over, you'll be back at home with us.

Your mother.

Thinking I am, at least, safe, I take the doctor's advice, keep calm and rest.

One afternoon, about an hour before tea, Mrs Clements comes to tell me someone wants to see me. 'In my sitting room,' she says.

Surprised both at an unannounced guest and at the honour of being allowed to use Matron's sitting room, I go up the stairs and open the door to her room.

A woman of about fifty years old, dressed in the kind of dress and jacket someone might wear to a meeting, stands up and holds out her hand. I can't remember her name. We shake hands. She's pleasant and informal. 'Sit down, Jane. I'm from the Church Moral Welfare Board. I'm on the committee of this home and I'm here because your mother has written to the Bishop…'

'She's done what?'

'You didn't know?'

'I haven't seen my mother recently. Things aren't too good at home and so I'm staying put here until the baby is born.'

She smiles. 'That's what you're here for.'

'Why did my mother write to the Bishop?'

'Your mother seems to think you're having too much of a good time here. She wants to know what we are doing to punish you.' She pauses to look out of the window. Her lips curve and I have the sense that she finds my mother's attitude amusing. 'She wants me to insist you go home at the weekends.'

Honestly, who does she think she is! I'm stammering. I'm so cross with my mother. 'I'm very sorry she's bothered you.'

'That's what I'm on the committee for. But this is an unusual request.' She looks at me and then comments, 'Rarely do we get a girl here who has suffered violence and then it's fairly obvious. You don't seem the type.' She colours slightly, and I can see she's distressed. 'Have your parents ever hit you because if they have…'

I have to stop her. I can't have her thinking bad things about my mother. It won't help. 'No, no,' I lie. 'They'd never do that.'

She shuffles a couple of papers she has in her hand and I can see one of them is a letter from the home. 'Mrs Clements says you've settled down well and follow the routine of the home. I'm not sure exactly what your mother has in mind, but punishment is not what we're here for.'

I try, 'I'm not sure either.'

'Most girls don't go home. Does your mother know that?'

'She's worried about me.' I can't think of anything else to say.

'Tell me about the father of the child.'

I tell her about Nick, how we met, what he did for a job. I don't mention Pa or Ma.

'I see. What are your plans?'

I find I can't tell her about that meeting with Nick. Whatever he has done, I can't be disloyal to the father of my baby. 'I was hoping we'd marry. His mother has offered us a home with her.'

'And his father?'

'They're separated.'

'I see.' Again, a pause, but this time as if she's not sure

what to say. Eventually she asks, 'And what if he lets you down?'

I know she's waiting to hear me say the correct thing. I want to say it. Although I still don't believe it will happen, not ever. So I cross my fingers in my lap and tell myself it's all right to lie. 'I'll give the baby up for adoption.'

She relaxes.

Her parting words are, 'I can't see what your mother is making all the fuss about. You seem a perfectly sensible young woman to me.'

Downstairs the bell rings for tea. They all know of course.

'Who was that?'

'What did she want?'

'Is it trouble from your mother?'

'Are you all right?'

More lies and this time to people I trust and I want to trust me. But I can't betray my mother. It's as if the horrible episodes at home will somehow melt away if I don't talk about them.

'I'm fine,' I say. 'It was a routine thing, just to check up on me.' Then I have a flash of inspiration. 'Because I've been here longer than normal. They had to send someone to check up on me.'

That satisfies them all.

We are in June. The month my baby will come into the world. Matinee jackets, cotton nightdresses, smock dresses, nappies, they are all ready. All I have to do is wait. In spite of everything, I am calm, resigned to my fate. For I can do nothing immediately to change it. I have no sense of what will happen after the delivery, but it doesn't bother me.

The sun shines from early morning until dusk. The air is thick, the birds silent as if even the small things couldn't be bothered to move. Women with large bumps are defeated.

The French windows on the far side of the lounge, beyond the dining table are left open and we spill out into the garden to stare at the wilting roses in sympathy. Mrs Clements produces deck chairs and opens them on the lawn and we sit in them or sprawl on the dry grass rubbing olive oil and vinegar on our tummies smelling, not as if we'd got a bun in the oven, but as though we are all frying tonight.

My baby settles upside down, with its bottom pointing to the way out. Attempts by the doctor to turn it fail.

In one corner of the garden there's a mock orange still with some flower blossoms. I inhale deeply, letting the scent take me back to the previous June when I lay under Nick on the common. Just me and Nick. No baby. No unwanted third person to complicate my life and make my future an unknown place, either a jungle with its mean, tangled vines of motherhood, marriage and penury or a waste land of no baby and still no love.

For I am not fooling myself that if I give my baby away my mother will forget and forgive. Last week, she rang me. I was allowed to take the call in Matron's office.

'How are you?'

'Fine.'

'What are you doing?'

'Waiting.'

'Have you heard from Nick?'

I didn't want to talk to her about Nick, not want to confess the outcome of our interview.

'No.'

'Oh Jane, what are you going to do?'

'It'll work out.'

'I think about this all the time. I worry about you constantly. You do know that don't you?'

'Mum, my hot chocolate is getting cold.' As I put down the handset, I imagined my mother standing in the hall staring at the wallpaper.

It's the fifteenth of June. My official expected date of delivery has arrived and gone.

After our housework is over, we stand round the dining room table to join in the fun. Since the room is full of laughter and chatter, anyone watching would think this is a joyous occasion

'This is so cute.' Julie holds up a blue matinee jacket. 'Could I have the pattern?'

'What's this?' Sandra holds up a pale blue, all-in-one garment, with a gathered top and short baggy legs.

Debbie says, 'A romper suit. Don't you have any?'

'No. What's it for?'

'Romping, what else?' Someone has a sense of humour.

'Naughty boy!'

More laughter.

On the table is an empty cardboard box from the kitchen. It contained boxes of cornflakes so is huge, the manufacturer's trade name, written in sloping red letters as if painted on with a giant brush.

Debbie is covering the lid of the box with blue baby wrapping paper, folding the edges of sheets down the sides of the lid, tucking them under and fixing them with sellotape.

She looks up and sees me. 'The ritual of sending your baby into the big wide world.' She's cheerful enough, not the person who, a week ago, had rushed from the room almost in tears.

Once the lid of the box is covered, the outside is wrapped in the same paper.

Then the packing begins. First a dozen terry nappies, with a couple of packets of nappy liners. Then three tiny white, brushed cotton nighties, their yokes embroidered with blue bunnies and yellow primroses. Next, in goes a collection of matinee jackets, tiny cardigans and a new pram suit.

'That's second size,' Debbie tells us proudly. 'All ready for autumn.'

Autumn. Debbie's baby will be settled with its new parents and Debbie back in a world where women don't get pregnant unless they have a husband, to a world of not needing a fake wedding ring or of living off national assistance. To a world of tight waists, slim skirts, new jobs and, maybe, a new flat. Debbie will have returned to the world outside the home. She'll be a career woman.

Is that all she will be? Will she, can she, forget? If I give up my baby for adoption, will I just flick back to the girl I was?

The box is full and the lid on. Finally, Debbie unrolls a wide, blue, satin ribbon, winds it twice around the box and ties a triumphant bow on the top. 'There,' she says, 'He's ready to go.'

'What time?' someone asks.

'Around twelve.' Her mouth twists and she begins to blink. A tear forms and tips onto her cheek. 'Time for his last feed.'

It was the custom to be discreet once the door bell had rung and the social worker was waiting in the hall. There were no 'Goodbyes' as if someone was leaving school, no cheers, no last-minute advice or messages of good luck.

I watched from the bedroom window.

The front door slammed and there was the driver carrying a suitcase, Debbie, cradling her baby Sam, and the social worker with the box adorned with the blue satin ribbon. They climbed into the taxi and left the home.

The rest of us mums-to-be were quieter than usual for the rest of that day. We had seen into our future.

'Jane, could I have a word?' Mrs Clements' voice echoes up the stairs as I climb towards my afternoon rest.

Hearing Mrs Clements use a sharper tone than usual, I turn and, holding the banister for support, step down again. My bump is heavy and uncomfortable, my baby either curling to sleep on my bladder or taking exercise by using my womb as a trampoline to bounce eager feet. I sleep solidly in the afternoons to wake at tea-time so refreshed that, for a moment, I forget everything. Only to have the cruel facts slap at me, chastising me for being so irresponsible as to forget for one instant.

I'm seventeen, pregnant and alone. No one, not my mother, my father or my lover wants me or my baby.

'Come in here.' Mrs Clements takes me into her office. 'Not that this is a secret, but I don't want everyone hearing. Sit down, that baby looks as if it's about to pop any minute.'

I sit in the low sofa wishing I could stay there forever.

'We're full up,' Mrs Clements says. 'I need to ask a favour.'

I can't think what she means and frown.

She goes on, 'There's a girl arriving later and I've nowhere for her to sleep.' She laughs. 'I assumed we'd have a new mum to move but none of you have cooperated.'

I feel myself flush. Is this my fault?

'I wondered if you'd mind sleeping in Sue's room for a couple of nights?'

'Sue's room?'

'She's having a short break to visit her parents and I have a feeling things will have changed by the time she returns. If you could take your things and camp for a couple of nights, I'd be grateful.'

Grateful? At last I can do something to repay all Mrs Clements' kindness to me. I smile at her, at the one person who has not said a harsh word to me and who now wants me to do her a favour.

I have never seen inside Sue's room. The nurse keeps herself away from us girls when she's not on duty, but it has to be a single room, with just the one bed. The thought of sleeping on my own again, even if just for a couple of nights, is heaven.

The room is perfect. On the top floor at the back of the house, it overlooks the garden. The bed is in a corner, covered with a patchwork quilt which I suspect is Sue's own. There's a dressing table and single wardrobe, but I dump my few clothes in a pile on the floor. I arrange my hairbrush and comb, my book and clock on the bedside table before I notice a door in the wall which doesn't look like a cupboard door. On the other side is a bathroom, the bath tucked under the eaves. A private bathroom. Such luxury. Folding up the patchwork quilt before I lie down for my afternoon nap, I promise myself a long, hot soak this evening.

Maybe that's what did it. In the early hours of the morning, still more than half asleep, I register mild discomfort, a tightening around my middle, a feeling of not having enough room inside myself for the baby and the supper I had eaten. I switch on the bedside lamp and look at my clock. Half past twelve.

By seven o'clock, with the morning sun promising another hot day, I know I am in labour. Pausing when my muscles squeeze like iron fingers round my abdomen, I pack my suitcase with a clean nightie, slippers and my sponge bag. I slip in a book before dressing and going downstairs.

There's a new face at the breakfast table but I am in no mood to be chatty. I wish Debbie was still here to give her advice. Should I eat breakfast, or will it make me sick? Would I need the energy a bowl of cornflakes heaped with sugar will give me? I manage a piece of toast and a cup of tea. I add sugar to that.

I push my plate away and put a hand on my abdomen. Which is crunching up in another contraction.

As Mrs Clements hands out the last letter, I put up my hand.

'What is it, Jane? Problems?'

'No problems, thank you. Just that the baby is coming.'

Eighteen

Memory makes an unreliable friend. Before that morning, I had never been taken anywhere by ambulance, but I don't remember a single detail about the journey. I can only assume that, as nothing untoward happened, I put it out of my head. I can't say whether I walked from the ambulance to the ward or whether I was pushed in a wheelchair. I don't remember getting undressed. But what I do recall is harshly clear in my mind.

I'm lying on a metal bed with rails at the bottom to stop my feet from poking off the end. The bed is in the centre of a small, oblong room. Apart from the door into the room from the corridor, there is a window through which I can see a wall with more windows in it, maybe overlooking a central well of the hospital, and a sink in the corner of the room. The floor is red linoleum and the walls are whitewashed.

I am alone and in pain, waiting for this event which has dominated my life for the last nine months. This event which I never believed would happen, not really. Silly as it sounds, I've always had this vision that something would happen to render the whole thing a horrendous nightmare. Of course, it didn't. So here I am.

I might as well have a table under my back for the comfort of this bed. When they put me on it, on not in because there are neither blankets nor a top sheet, the sheet stretched across the mattress was crisp and cool. Now it's creased and feels damp under my skin. I've been lying here for two hours. There's a huge, round clock with a white face, black roman numerals and a cream plastic frame on the wall opposite me. It has a minute hand and I've been watching this thin black line at its labours for a hundred and twenty movements. It tells me it is now half-past twelve. The girls will be sitting down to lunch.

I'm wearing one of those hospital gowns, tied behind with tape. The two knots dig into my back but, apart from that, I'm more or less naked. As the next contraction comes, I close my eyes. When I open them, there's a hugely fat woman in a pink nurses' dress standing beside me yanking the overall up over my legs.

'Knees up!' The nurse uses sergeant major talk.

'Sorry?'

'Knees up and open!'

As I obey her, the checked cotton garment preserving my modesty rucks further up my body and my bump appears. Round and very hard, it's a human melon. Even the skin is shiny.

'What's happening?' My voice is thin, weak and sounds far away, as if it has nothing to do with today, with this empty, cold room or with me and my bump. A sudden contraction waves through my back. I'd double up in pain but I'm not a contortionist and drawing my knees higher doesn't help. The pain starts at either side of my spine and reaches round like two sets of steel fingers to clamp my flesh to my ribs.

'Hurts, doesn't it?' the sergeant major says. Compassion is not her middle name.

I nod.

'Didn't think of that, did you? The last time you were lying on your back with your legs open nine months ago?'

For just a moment I don't understand her. This is the first time I've gone into labour and right now this will be the last time. Forget any other last time. Then her words make sense.

'Perhaps you'll think better of it next time. Sex isn't all it's cracked up to be and now you've landed yourself with this mess.'

I stare at her, understanding that she thinks it's her duty to chastise me. I haven't the strength to defy her. Anyway, she has a point. I am in a mess and was it worth it? Probably not. So I stick to, 'What's happening now?'

'I've got to shave you, haven't I? I get all the nasty jobs. You just lie there. Don't you worry about anything.'

This final instruction is given with such a sneer of contempt I'm left in no doubt I should have worried a great deal more nine months ago.

The water is tepid, the soap smells of disinfectant and the razor feels blunt. Trying not to count the number of scrapes against my skin nor to register the sore nicks as the blade catches me, I lie still, gazing at the bright, round light bulb stuck in its socket in the ceiling directly above me.

'That's you done.' The sergeant major tips the hairy water down the sink in the corner of the room.

Another contraction threatens, and I instinctively double my back, half sitting.

At least the woman is good enough to give me some advice. 'Try running round the bed.'

'Can I?'

'Do what you like. Isn't that how you got here? By pleasing yourself?' She marches out, taking the accoutrements of her trade with her.

Walking is better than lying; running is great and I'm circling the bed as though training for the Olympics when a young man, quite dishy, tall with dark hair and a smile, wearing a proper white overall with buttons down the front, comes in.

'And what are you up to, young lady?'

Young lady! I stop running and hold onto the rail at the foot of the bed. I am short of breath and panting. My cheeks feel hot and I must look a right mess. But that terrible pain has gone, that stiffness which clamped my body has relaxed. I can feel a new contraction approaching so I take deeper breaths and wait. I'd like to climb on the bed but there's no way I'm turning my back on the doctor and letting him catch sight of my bare bum, so I stand while my contraction squeezes my bump into the shape of a rugby ball. The foot rail is cold under my fingers and then slippery as my sweat runs.

'Is the pain bad?' he asks.

I nod. Words are impossible.

'Would you like an injection?'

208

I give him my best beseeching look. I can't believe he's being kind to me. I put his offer down to making his own life easier but I'll accept it nevertheless. When the contraction is over, and my body looks normal for a nine-month gone pregnant woman, I add, 'Anything to help would be fine.'

'Hop on the bed then.'

I do a good imitation of an elephant skipping and find myself lying on the bed, the overall modestly tucked underneath me, covering me up. The needle in my arm is sharp, the effect sweet. I manage a whimper of gratitude for the doctor before the onset of another contraction tenses the muscles in my face. I breathe and pull my lips into a taught smile.

He puts a hand on my swollen belly and waits. There's a nurse with him, not the military kind but a young woman wearing a wide, red belt round her waist. A waist that is enviably thin. The doctor says to the nurse, 'Not long to go now. Keep an eye on her, will you?'

But then they both walk out of the room without a backward glance.

And I thought the nurse might stay and hold my hand. Stupid of me. Tears fill my eyes. I am ashamed of my cowardice. I am not the first woman to have a baby and there must be others, today, in other small rooms on this floor, waiting for their babies to arrive. For babies which are wanted. For babies who'll have a right to be here. For babies who'll have a home to go to. We are abandoned. Tears run down my cheeks.

Outside, through the only window in the room, high up, between a tower and a chimney stack, I see a vertical band of blue sky. It reminds me of photos in travel brochures; those illustrations which you don't quite believe for their intense colour. Somewhere, then, the sun is shining. But it's not in this room, in this off-white isolation. On this glorious, sunny day in June I'm going to have my baby. And I'm not saying I'm gloomy about this because I'm not. At least it'll be over and done with.

However, as I lie here and feel the contractions move round my abdomen to the front of my bump, as I almost enjoy the sensation of the power without the pain, I know that today isn't the end. It won't be over with today will it? The rest of it will be just beginning.

I look at the clock. It's just after half-past one. I put a hand on my bump and wonder about Nick.

'It's just the two of us,' I whisper. 'You and me.'

The muscles round my tummy clench in a tight hug. A new pain, seeming to start at my edges and work towards my middle, makes me cry out.

Red-belt sticks her head round the door. 'OK?'

This seems to demand that I answer 'Yes' but I shake my head. 'No.'

Her black-shoed feet cross the floor swiftly and silently. She pushes back my overall and issues the command, 'Knees up.'

I obey and she peers between my legs into my interior making me feel as though my body belongs to someone else. Then she pushes three fingers inside me and moves them around. 'You're ready. This bun is ready to come out of the oven.'

After all the arguing and debating, all the pain and humiliation, unaware of the controversy it has caused, this baby is arriving in its own time. As we wait for someone to help the nurse push the bed into the delivery room, I wonder if I am about to become the mother of a little boy or a little girl.

Help arrives in the shape of a young male orderly, tall with a spotty complexion. He looks embarrassed and kicks at the break on the wheels of the bed. I ride along the corridor towards a second room almost identical to the last one but bigger. The furniture is the same. A sink in the corner, a narrow bed in the centre of the room and a clock on the wall.

'Can you get off this bed and onto the delivery table?' red-belt nurse asks me.

I nod but as I pull myself up, the wave of the next contraction is so powerful I flop back on the bed, crying out loud. I'm aware of a flood of warmth and wetness underneath me. I prop myself on my elbows and stare at a quickly spreading pool of pale yellow dampness.

'I've wet myself,' I say, sounding infantile and pathetic.

'Quick,' says the nurse. 'Her waters have broken.' There is more than a small degree of urgency in her voice. She somehow manages to hook her arms under my arm-pits and the young man lifts me by slipping his arms under my knees. There's an awkward moment when I don't seem to be able to leave the bed behind but then I'm on the delivery table. Lying flat with no pillow under my head, my bump looms huge and peculiarly knobbled. I reach out and touch it. Without the watery protection, my baby's bones are hard and, for the first time, I realize that what is coming next will hurt.

'Another injection or gas and air?' the nurse asks me.

Her gentle tone of voice only makes me feel more vulnerable. 'What's best?'

'Gas, really. We don't want a floppy baby, do we?' And she bustles off to get whatever is necessary.

I lie on the table holding my legs together like I'm keeping myself for my wedding night. I look at the clock again and see that already I've been in this room for ten minutes. I think that babies take about an hour to actually get out. And I'm frightened.

A nurse in a blue uniform returns pushing a trolley with a gas cylinder on it and a long rubber tube with a mouthpiece on the end of it. She leaves this at the head end of the delivery table and waits. Red-belt returns and each one takes one of my feet and straps them to metal props at the end of the table. They pull my gown up and away from my legs to leave me exposed. Red-belt hands me the gas mouthpiece.

'If it hurts, put this over your mouth and breathe deeply,' she tells me. 'When the next contraction comes try pushing.'

It comes pretty quickly. Tentatively, I put the mask over my mouth and try breathing in and pushing at the same time. The contraction takes over, squeezing me, kneading me, hurting me. The pain is sharp and so fierce. My baby feels stuck fast. The fear grows, and I cry out in uncontrolled terror.

The blue nurse holds my hand. 'You're fighting your own body. Take in some gas and air first and then when the pain comes push and breath out.'

That's better. I feel a power, a strength which is a completely new experience. The pain is there but is not so sharp and nasty. The next contraction comes fast behind the first one. I stop checking the clock, shut my eyes, breathe in and out and push harder.

'It's coming.'

I think that's the red-belt nurse. My head is muzzy with the gas and air but I'm conscious of the tension in my bump lessening, of the baby moving towards the outside world. My fear is still there but it has been overtaken by a struggle in which I am only one half of the whole.

The contractions come one after the other. The pain envelopes me completely. I give into the screaming but the voice I hear isn't mine. It echoes around the room, it calls for help, it calls for an end to this torture. My body is one big squeeze box. It wants to rid itself of the new life inside it, but the new life seems reluctant to take the hint.

I open my eyes. Red-belt is peering up my legs again. She puts a hand on my left knee and parts my legs even more. The clock ticks. The three of us wait. A contraction comes and goes. The angles of bone under my skin don't move.

The other nurse's voice is hoarse. 'Shall we get some help?'

The red-belt is staring into my vagina. She should be seeing a baby's head. Even I know that. She's staring as though she's looking at a monster. 'I can see a foot,' she says and runs from the room.

The remaining nurse, who suddenly looks much too young and inexperienced for this agony, smiles at me. 'Don't worry,' she says. 'You'll be fine.'

I want to scream, 'Never mind me. What about my baby?' But I don't. I hold my breath and bite my lip. Ironically, I suddenly remember Rita and her oval, white pills with the deadly brown powder inside. And I now know why I didn't swallow one. Forget Nick. Forget my mother or my father. Forget the other girls in the home. All I want is my baby. To have and to hold. For better or worse. Until death do us part. The clock now says ten to three. And we wait, me, and my baby. We wait for the help which is so slow in arriving. And I'm frightened.

I read somewhere that being born was more dangerous than dying. At least with the dying you're expecting it. Birth should be the beginning, not the end of life. It isn't always.

A voice from the corridor proclaims it's too late to turn it. The doctor arrives, already wearing a mask, pulling on rubber gloves, rolling them up to his wrists with a snap. 'On the next contraction push hard,' he tells me.

The next one clutches at my abdomen, mounts my body, an independent force, a creature of steel with fingers long and thin but so strong, strong enough to push a baby. I take a deep breath and expel the air with a great bearing down.

My son is born at three o'clock in the afternoon.

I watch as they carry him to a room across the corridor and blow down his lungs with pipes; blow and suck, blow and suck.

The blue nurse runs back to me. 'What were you going to call him?'

Were…

'Simon Benedict.' That was what Nick and I agreed, when we were in the world of dreams.

I look on as she dips her forefinger into a glass of water, her voice clear enough for me to hear. 'I baptise you Simon Benedict.'

The doctor stops sucking, and the nurse closes the door.

The clock tells me it is a quarter past three.

Nineteen

My diary has a full account of the day my son was born. When did I write it, I wonder? Did I have the presence of mind to pack the volume in my bag? The entry reads as if it were written immediately following the events.

Contractions began at midnight and I left for the hospital at 8.30.

A technical account. Later I write, *Nick came in to see me directly after I had been stitched.*

This I remember. I was shocked he was there and so promptly. He told me that Mrs Clements had rung him to say that I had gone in. I wrote that he was upset and cried, staying with me until supper time.

They put me in a side room. They didn't say so, but I knew why. I was, once more, different, not a proper mother, just a mishap, a hospital statistic no one wanted to mention. I lay on my narrow, high bed listening to the noises of the main ward: babies crying, women cooing, nurses asking, 'And how is Mother today?' And I waited.

Sister gave me a sleeping pill. 'It's routine,' she said. 'All mothers have one night's good sleep. The doctor will write you up for milk pills.'

'Milk pills?'

'To dry up your milk.'

My parents visited me the next day, but, in my diary, I made no mention of their attitude towards me. I must have told them Nick had been to see me because, a couple of days later, I had a deputation of my doctor, the ward sister and a junior nurse. My father had rung the doctor to instruct him that Nick should not be allowed to see me again. I wrote that this made me angry but also embarrassed. I apologised to the doctor for my father's behaviour.

By the third day I was writing, Feel better today. I don't feel so unhappy. I think it was shock and sudden disappointment that made me feel down.

At one point, Sister asked me if I'd seen my parents.

I nodded.

'We usually only let fathers come on the first few days, but we make an exception for you girls.'

I blushed. I was still one of the girls marked out as a sore, a slight nuisance, someone everyone would rather do without.

Sister tugged my sheet straight. 'Is that all right? Are you happy to see your parents?'

'Of course.'

'It's only that some girls don't want that. We don't like any trouble.'

'Are you saying that if I didn't want them to visit me you could prevent it?'

She picked up my notes. 'We couldn't. You're under age. Still, it's best to be sure.'

Under age or not, it seems I am old enough to deal with the registrar, who arrives later in the week and is polite to me. 'Good afternoon.'

'I'm under age, you know.'

He sits with a huge book on his lap and looks at me with surprise. 'Under age for what?' and here he colours, 'I hope you're not confiding something of an intimate nature to me.'

My turn to blush. 'I'm not under sixteen. But I am under twenty-one.'

'I'm here to register the birth of your baby, not marry you.' He smiles. 'Don't worry. Only you can do this, no one else. You don't need anyone's permission or help. Except perhaps mine.' He smiles again, and I almost fall in love with him.

He opens his book at a fresh page. 'I need your full name, the name of your baby and the date of birth.'

'The baby was born on the fifteenth of June. At three o'clock.'

'The exact time I don't need. You had a little boy?'

'Yes.' I'm feeling important, wanted and grown up. This is an official record and I'm contributing to it. On my own. With no one else here.

'Your baptised name?'

I give it to him.

'The name of the baby?'

I give that to him.

'I have just one more question.'

I nod. I daren't speak. The tears which I haven't cried since the birth are threatening and I know that once I let them, they'll flood out.

'Are you registering the name of the baby's father?'

I gulp and steady my voice. 'Do I have a choice?'

'You're not married, are you?'

This is surer ground. I'm not married. I say, 'No.' Now it's truly out in the open I feel better. About myself, about my situation and much better about my baby.

The Registrar is saying, 'It's up to you. Either way. We can put the father's name in or I strike through the box.' He waits. When I don't answer he says gently, 'It's entirely up to you. Which would you prefer?'

I hear my voice, calm and clear. 'Leave it blank.'

He strikes a diagonal line through the box.

'And now, I understand, we have to register a death.'

I hadn't thought, hadn't expected this. But of course. Simon was alive for fifteen minutes. I didn't even hold him.

The registrar must sense my hesitation, for he says quietly, 'You can leave this for now if you want to but you will have to come to the Town Hall fairly soon. Again, it's up to you.'

I imagine my father's face as I ask him to drive me anywhere, let alone to do this. I shake my head and blow my nose. 'I'd rather go home with everything tidied up,' I say. 'We'll do it now.'

◆ ◆ ◆

'You asleep?'

The stage whisper can only be one person. And just in time. Tomorrow I'm leaving hospital. I open my eyes and sit up. 'Rita.'

She's holding a bunch of roses, which she puts on my locker. 'Show me the flat tum then?'

I pull back the bed covers.

Rita presses the palm of her hand on my stomach. 'Pretty good. Taking your milk pills?'

My mouth drops. 'How on earth…?'

She laughs. 'Don't say I can still surprise you? Trust your Auntie Rita to know most things.' Then she opens her bag and pulls out a copy of Tom Jones. 'Now you don't have to do an exam in it I thought you might like to finish it.'

It's a kind thought, and I take the book. 'How's the revision going?'

Rita shrugs. 'OK. I'll be glad when it's all over.'

She tells me her plans. Secretarial College, then a temporary job to pay for language tuition in French, Spanish and Russian and, finally, a job abroad. 'A diploma in professional and executive services.' She laughs. 'I hope.' Then she adds, 'If I went to the States, language wouldn't be a problem, but I have a hunch international secretaries will be the future thing.'

Dear Rita. That was to be the last time I saw her although I often wonder whether she made it into her dream world of bosses in grey suits with sexy secretaries. Knowing Rita, I bet she soon tired of typing men's words and found a way of typing her own.

I had visits from the girls at the home, Mrs Clements, two of my former teachers from my school and a second visit from my parents. We talked about my plans and, somehow, I agreed to apply for a post in the civil service. It was to please my father. I still couldn't decide how to please my mother, or even if I wanted to.

So that was it. No more tears. No offer of counselling. Just sharp realism.

Nick did come to the hospital once more before I left. I might have enjoyed his company and laughed with him, as it says in the diary, but I felt removed from him, distanced maybe, by my experiences of having a child and then not having one. I know, if I am honest, that I was relieved.

It was to be the last time I saw the father of my child.

In those days, the statutory length of a hospital stay after the birth ended on the tenth day. If a baby was born before midday, that day counted as Day 1. Since my baby was born during the afternoon, I had a full nine days of lying in bed.

I was discharged during the doctors' nine o'clock ward rounds. Using the hospital telephone trolley, I rang home. My father collected me later in the morning, bringing my school navy pleated skirt and a white tennis shirt. The skirt fitted.

While I collected my things from the home and said 'Goodbye' to the girls, he waited in the car outside. Sue told me Mrs Clements was on holiday. Again, I was relieved. I wasn't sure how I would say goodbye to her. She was the one adult who had been kind to me throughout my weeks at the home, yet another person I was never to see again. Later, I wrote to her.

My life was undergoing a metamorphosis.

Before lunch, the final ceremony had to be performed. My mother, without giving me so much as a welcome home kiss, took me by the hand and led me into the back garden.

'Hello, anyone there?' she called over the fence.

Our next door neighbour duly appeared at her back door, standing on tiptoe so she could see us.

'Look,' said my mother, beaming. 'Here's Jane. I told you there was nothing wrong.'

Our neighbour beamed at me. I beamed back. The charade was complete.

I'll risk losing the good will of my readers if I am honest, but this story is nothing if not honest. I cried when my baby died but I didn't cry for very long.

For what would I have done if he had lived? Could I have faced giving him up for adoption? Would I be as strong as the girls I had known in the home? I feared not. I was an innocent, totally naive in the ways of welfare benefits, finding a home, making ends meet, bringing up a child. I was certain that my mother would not help me but maybe I am doing her an injustice in saying that now. I could have been wrong.

All these troubles were taken out of my hands. On the day of my discharge from hospital, I dressed and went home. It was as simple as that. I got on with my life.

Life has had its problems, but nothing compared with the life of a single mother bringing up a child on her own. I might have met a man willing to take on another man's baby but that is the land of fantasy and I am sticking to the truth here.

Twenty

In November 1942, after a series of defeats from Dunkirk to Singapore, Winston Churchill told the House of Commons, 'Now this is not the end. It is not even the beginning of the end. But it is, perhaps, the end of the beginning.'

My return home marked the end of my beginning, the end of my childhood. For my mother's peace of mind, I was compelled to live with a story that I thought, at the time, I would forever have to keep secret. After all, wasn't that the point of going to the home, of the subterfuge and, yes, the lies?

Not that I analysed my situation at the time. I was just glad to be home, thankful all the trouble had not caused a permanent rift between my parents and me and looking forward to the future whatever it might hold.

I did not look back. If that sounds harsh, that is how it was.

My mother and I made up our differences through a muddle of ignoring the past and settling for a silent agreement that she wouldn't ask me probing questions about my boyfriends and I wouldn't test her patience by going out with boys she and my father didn't approve of.

As the weeks, months and years passed, various incidents helped me to move on, as they say nowadays.

It's early evening, after supper, shortly after my discharge. My father's watching a sit-com on the television while my mother is in the breakfast room sewing. I've put my record player at the other end of the table and we are listening to my LP of West Side Story. The track is Somewhere, a romantic and sentimental song about two young lovers, from different backgrounds, who are rejected by both their families.

At the finish of the song, my mother gives a great sigh. 'Oh Jane, maybe we did the wrong thing. Maybe we should have let you marry Nick right from the start.'

Her sentimental take on my sorry story angers me but I don't show it, just say, 'Don't be silly. It wouldn't have been for the best. Anyway, it's all over now so let's just forget it.'

I'm not entirely convinced I mean it, but I'm sure it's the right thing to say to my mother, to encourage her to think everything's fine.

On my nineteenth birthday, I'm taken to the Old Vic by the man who will become my husband. We see Albert Finney in A Flea in her Ear. We watch the entire performance standing up. He is a student. I don't care about the discomfort. I'm enjoying the evening.

We go for several more dates, a dinner-dance at a Chinese restaurant in Soho, his graduation ball plus simple things like a picnic in Kew Gardens, sherry from the wood at a London pub and a further drink or two out in the country, where we have our first kiss. And talk.

My mother can tell I'm happy. But she can't leave it at that. She can't forget or let me forget.

'It's all very well, Jane,' she says one morning after I've seen him, 'But what do you think he's going to say when you tell him about the baby?'

I'm interested that she assumes I am going to tell him but irritated at her interference in something which should be a private matter between the two of us. I have the last word.

'I don't have to think,' I announce. 'Because I've already told him.'

She doesn't say another word. Ever.

Before the wedding, my mother makes plain her forgiveness by taking me to lunch with Fiona in Dickens and Jones, a smart department store at the top of Regents Street.

The restaurant is from a time already passing, of ladies who shop still wearing tight-waisted suits, high heels and hats. Fiona wears a more up to date shorter skirt and blazer, but she's looking faded.

We eat plaice and chips followed by ice-cream sundaes and drink water.

And make small talk. My mother recalls holidays we've enjoyed recently, a trip to Switzerland and a week in Cornwall, by the sea. Fiona rebuts the idea that she's about to marry her latest man and I tell her about my job in the home civil service and my plans to take an internal exam to gain early promotion. My mother beams. It is as if none of it ever happened.

I learnt to glaze over the truth. 'No, I didn't go to university. I wanted to get out into the real world. Anyway, I didn't do well enough in my A levels.' Most of that was the truth, just a massaged version of it. For over fifty years no one knew of my story, no friends, no relations, and certainly no work colleagues.

Do I regret what I did and what happened to me? I certainly regret that I wasted my early love on a lazy youth with his head in the clouds. Do I regret making my mother so unhappy? Of course I do, but how much of her unhappiness was of her own making? Did she have it in her to love me enough to support me in my decisions at that time? I honestly think she didn't have the emotional resources to cope. That helps me to forgive.

Do I regret the pregnancy? I was forced to grow-up quickly. Nothing that happened to me in the future could ever be so traumatic. That knowledge protected me against difficult times for the rest of my life.

Most of all, I learnt much about people, some similar to me, some quite different and from such a variety of backgrounds. I learnt it was possible to be cheerful, even happy, in adversity. I learnt to forgive. My mother and myself. Most of that learning took place while I was living in the mother-and-baby home.

That special place was, as they say now, a facilitator.

About a week after I'd returned from the mother-and-baby home, the post brought two envelopes, a brown one and a white one. My father slit the white one open, took out a letter and a small card, which he handed to my mother with the words, 'I'll put it away.'

My mother glanced at the card before holding it out to me. 'It's all you've got. Don't show it to anyone else.'

I read the words Merton and Morden Cemetery and the number on the card: 40268/28. The number of my baby's grave. I handed it back to my mother. 'You keep it.'

She did, and I didn't expect to see it again. However, after her death, I discovered my diary and the letters at the bottom of her trunk. I also found the envelope containing the small, square card. It was mine. To do with it as I wanted. My first reaction was to throw it away, rather than indulge in sad thoughts and useless regrets. I had a choice.

The cemetery was like any other London burial ground. I walked past elaborate carvings of angels and crosses, and then plainer graves with only a headstone and, finally, in one corner of the ground, a row of tiny grassed mounds each with a metal-framed card printed with a number. I found the grave and stood, looking down on it. I tried to cry but why cry now? Soon, I walked back between the memorials and out of the gate.

I read somewhere that those anonymous mounds usually represented a communal grave. A thought I found strangely cheering. At least he wasn't alone.

Twenty-One

One aspect of this story is the tense relationship between my mother and me, an illustration of what was known as the generation gap.

My mother, christened Ivy, certainly comes over as a most unloving and uncaring, if not cruel, person, seeing situations only from her own perspective. That was not her whole person.

I was married with children by the time she told me her story. It was not a happy one and led me to forgive her any wrong she had done me. I have recorded my side of the story. I owe it to her to reveal the aspects of her life which explain her attitudes and actions.

My maternal grandmother had nine children, eight of whom survived. Her husband owned and ran a shop from one of the front rooms of their house in Hill Street, Hastings. It was a general store, common in those days, selling everything from smaller items of clothing to groceries, tea, sugar, butter, sweets. Money was scarce, and life was hard for my grandmother.

In those circumstances, it was the custom for the family to send one child to live with relations, a family who had spare capacity and a desire to be helpful. The child would remain there until the time was right for him or her to be returned home.

One of my aunts told me how Ivy, still a youngster, took up sewing, sending her sisters out to buy cotton, zips or ribbon. She ended with, 'Of course we missed her when she was sent away.' I knew my mother had spent some time away from home, when she was young, but I assumed she was referring to a short holiday, never dreaming she left her home and family for several years.

At a very young age, Ivy was sent to live with her grandmother, whose husband was a Strict and Particular Baptist, the Pastor of his own church, The Ebenezer Chapel on Tackleway.

Strict and Particular Baptists are what the label says. Their Believer's Rule of conduct is governed by the Gospel, not the law of the land. Sundays are spent mostly in chapel, two full services plus afternoon Sunday school. All food eaten that day is cold, since no cooking on The Sabbath is allowed by God. Apart from the visits to Chapel, the people remain indoors, reading only the Bible and sewing samplers of religious tracts. Children are not allowed to play with other children.

My mother talked to me briefly about her life with her grandparents. Years of living as an only child when she had sisters at home, no hobbies except reading the Bible and sewing. No wonder she knew all the Books of the Bible off by heart and would recite them if I asked her. She was also an excellent needle woman.

When my mother was eleven years old she won a scholarship to Hastings Grammar, an academic school.

This had not been achieved by any of her elder siblings, although the two youngest boys in the family did follow in her footsteps. She told me that my grandmother had signed a form committing her daughter to schooling until she was sixteen.

However, just before my mother's fourteenth birthday, she was informed that she was to be sent out to work.

Her response was, 'What about the piece of paper to say I would stay at school until I was sixteen?'

My grandmother replied, 'Never mind about any piece of paper. I've found you a job.'

Ivy was sent away a second time, not to live with a member of her family but with strangers, to care for their two young children, one of whom was a baby, and to sleep in the attic next to the cold-water tank.

My grandmother's one piece of advice was, 'Girl, if you bring trouble back to this house, I'll beat the living daylights out of you.'

When, I ask myself, did she have the chance to learn how to love?

At least she had some education, which promised well for her future.

Eventually, she left Hastings for London. For a bit of glamour in her life, she worked in a couturier's, modeling the clothes to customers, while she improved her dressmaking skills. When she preferred to earn more money, she worked as a waitress in Lyons' Corner House near the Strand. At some point, she learnt shorthand typing.

The Second World War came, and she enlisted in the WAAF, soon being commissioned as an officer. Her version of that was, 'I couldn't see the difference between myself and the other officers, so I knocked on the commander's door and asked to be promoted.'

I'm not sure it was quite so easy but, however she did it, she did it and her new, posh friends gave her self-confidence. Wartime was the best time of her life. That became her mantra.

She learnt codes and cyphers. She told me, 'I was stationed at Leighton Buzzard.' Close to Bletchley Park but, although family tradition has it that she worked at Bletchley, I can't find any evidence of her being stationed there. An aunt said to me recently, 'Ivy was at Bletchley Park, wasn't she?' I nodded. Now she is no longer with me, I don't want to take away from her any glories family tradition has awarded.

'I was with Churchill,' was another of her proudest achievements and certainly I have photographs of her in Italy when he was there during the war.

What is certain is that she met my father, a captain in the British army, in Italy. They married, lived in Italy for two years, returning to England when my mother was pregnant with me. They moved in with her widowed mother-in-law in Hertfordshire.

Sadly, she was never accepted by her mother-in-law, who delighted in telling her that her son had been married before and was a divorced man. Even though it was his first wife who was at fault by running off with a GI, being married to a divorcee made her a social pariah in her village. Denied membership of the Church of England's Mother's Union, not welcomed at the Holy Communion table, she was isolated and lonely.

However, she made her own social ladder. My father ran a local dramatic society with my mother playing the leading lady most of the time. She gave successful parties, she ran a cake stall at the annual Boy Scouts' fete, made all her own clothes, and sometimes garments for other women, from Vogue patterns. She was smart and attractive.

Eventually she escaped the prejudices of 1950s village life. When I was sixteen, we moved to London. My father had gained promotion and they celebrated by buying a house, not in the smartest area of Streatham, but good enough for my mother to think she had, finally, arrived. She convinced the headmistress of a comprehensive school in Fulham to take her on as a domestic science teacher because, 'Your girls need someone like me.' In those days that was possible. I remember her telling me stories of having to break up fights between the girls in the classroom.

She was in her prime, doing well and knowing it. Her one aim was not to drop back into the world of deprivation from which she had come.

Then she discovered she had a daughter who had lied to her and broken the most fundamental rule of not keeping her virginity to give away on her wedding night. I had brought trouble onto her house.

Her whole world crumbled.

She couldn't cope. My father wasn't much help. I think he was embarrassed.

If my mother could have confided in her sisters, she would have found support. As it turned out, I was not the only girl in the family to become pregnant outside wedlock. But my mother was so ashamed of what I had done that she kept her plight secret. Until it didn't matter. Until it was all over. Then she told all her sisters!

As I was going through puberty, I'd realised she was afraid of me growing up. She couldn't deal with my emerging sexuality. She certainly did not expect me to take matters into my own hands. When I did, it shook her to her very core and changed her from being a settled, if over emotional, person, to a woman with a shameful secret. She had to protect herself from public knowledge of her situation. She had to fight and the person she fought was me.

After it was all over, we became uneasy friends. My wedding photos show a smiling mother of the bride, wearing the dusky pink suit she had made herself.

In her last years, my mother developed dementia. When I finally took her to live in a home, did she remember the day she left me at the mother-and-baby home?

I will never know. There are many things in life we never know for certain and hence never fully understand.

My mother died in October 2002 after hearing the news that she was a great-grandmother. She was content.

When I became a mother, I thought myself into her skin. To go through all that she had, to strive for a better life, to think she had found it with my father, to discover he'd deceived her about his past marriage, to have a daughter who seemed to be set for university and a career and then to watch that daughter throw it all away.

She was angry and hurt, but more than that she was deeply ashamed and furious that I had brought such disgrace into the home.

So it was for thousands of other mothers up and down the country, who had lived through the war and survived, who had bettered themselves and who were looking forward to a peaceful old age with married children and grandchildren. But not before they watched their lives temporarily crumble.

Twenty-Two

I was married with two children when, one morning, alone in the house, I listened to a phone-in programme on the radio. The subject was adopted children seeking their birth mothers. Not of particular interest to me. Until the next caller spoke. It was a man, I guessed a forty-something. His words cut to my heart.

> *'I can't forgive my mother.'*
> *Presenter: 'Your birth mother?'*
> *Man: 'How could she do such a terrible thing?'*
> *Presenter: 'What did she do?'*
> *Man: 'She gave me away. She abandoned me.'*
> *Presenter: 'Why do you think she did that?'*
> *Man: 'She didn't love me. I certainly don't want to find her. And I will never forgive her.'*

Asked about the strength of his rejection of his mother, whether he felt any sympathy for her, he didn't waver. Convinced that she had simply abandoned him, he hated her. He refused to consider how difficult her life would be as an unmarried mother, or why she took her decision to have her child adopted. He didn't seem to be able to imagine how impossible things would be for her with, almost certainly, little money and even less family and public sympathy. Or for him, how being branded illegitimate, would stigmatise him.

His mother believed she did the very best for him, ensuring he'd grow up in a stable and loving family. By giving him away, she proved her love.

The presenter invited listeners to call in. I could tell the young man that he was completely wrong about the love. I could tell him about those brown envelopes, the journey to an office where the mothers saw their baby for the last time, no goodbyes, no wishes of good luck, just a silent acceptance of the way things had to be.

I rang the number and was put through to a researcher who asked me about my interest in the subject.

I took a deep breath and began, 'I had a baby when…' but I broke down. I couldn't say it. Even after all those years, I couldn't talk about my secret. However much I longed to explain, I couldn't speak it aloud. I failed that man.

I hope my story goes some way to explaining to those adults who, as babies, were put up for adoption. My story is not everyone's story, but I am sure, from the girls I met in the mother and baby home, that unmarried mothers back then were convinced they were making the best choice for their babies. The babies they loved with all their hearts.

I hope this book helps him, and all the others like him, to forgive.